www.EffortlessMath.com

... So Much More Online!

✓ FREE Math lessons

✓ More Math learning books!

✓ Mathematics Worksheets

✓ Online Math Tutors

Need a PDF version of this book?

Visit www.EffortlessMath.com

TASC

Mathematics

Prep 2019

A Comprehensive Review and Ultimate Guide to the TASC Math Test

By

Reza Nazari & Ava Ross

All inquiries should be addressed to:

info@effortlessMath.com

www.EffortlessMath.com

ISBN-13: 978-1-970036-11-4

ISBN-10: 1-970036-11-7

Published by: Effortless Math Education

www.EffortlessMath.com

Description

TASC Mathematics Prep 2019 provides students with the confidence and math skills they need to succeed on the TASC Math, building a solid foundation of basic Math topics with abundant exercises for each topic. It is designed to address the needs of TASC test takers who must have a working knowledge of basic Math.

This comprehensive book with over 2,500 sample questions and 2 complete TASC tests is all you need to fully prepare for the TASC Math. It will help you learn everything you need to ace the math section of the TASC.

Effortless Math unique study program provides you with an in-depth focus on the math portion of the test, helping you master the math skills that students find the most troublesome.

This book contains most common sample questions that are most likely to appear in the mathematics section of the TASC.

Inside the pages of this comprehensive TASC Math book, students can learn basic math operations in a structured manner with a complete study program to help them understand essential math skills. It also has many exciting features, including:

- Dynamic design and easy-to-follow activities
- A fun, interactive and concrete learning process
- Targeted, skill-building practices
- Fun exercises that build confidence
- Math topics are grouped by category, so you can focus on the topics you struggle on
- All solutions for the exercises are included, so you will always find the answers
- 2 Complete TASC Math Practice Tests that reflect the format and question types on TASC

TASC Mathematics Prep 2019 is an incredibly useful tool for those who want to review all topics being covered on the TASC test. It efficiently and effectively reinforces learning outcomes through engaging questions and repeated practice, helping you to quickly master basic Math skills.

About the Author

Reza Nazari is the author of more than 100 Math learning books including:
– **Math and Critical Thinking Challenges:** For the Middle and High School Student
– **GED Math in 30 Days**
– **ASVAB Math Workbook 2018 - 2019**
– **Effortless Math Education Workbooks**
– **and many more Mathematics books ...**

Reza is also an experienced Math instructor and a test–prep expert who has been tutoring students since 2008. Reza is the founder of Effortless Math Education, a tutoring company that has helped many students raise their standardized test scores—and attend the colleges of their dreams. Reza provides an individualized custom learning plan and the personalized attention that makes a difference in how students view math.

You can contact Reza via email at:
reza@EffortlessMath.com

Find Reza's professional profile at:
goo.gl/zoC9rJ

Contents

Chapter 1: Fundamentals and Building Blocks

Topics that you'll learn in this chapter:

- ✓ Simplifying Fractions
- ✓ Adding and Subtracting Fractions
- ✓ Multiplying and Dividing Fractions
- ✓ Adding Mixed Numbers
- ✓ Subtract Mixed Numbers
- ✓ Multiplying Mixed Numbers
- ✓ Dividing Mixed Numbers
- ✓ Comparing Decimals

- ✓ Rounding Decimals
- ✓ Adding and Subtracting Decimals
- ✓ Multiplying and Dividing Decimals
- ✓ Converting Between Fractions, Decimals and Mixed Numbers
- ✓ Factoring Numbers
- ✓ Greatest Common Factor
- ✓ Least Common Multiple

"A Man is like a fraction whose numerator is what he is and whose denominator is what he thinks of himself. The larger the denominator, the smaller the fraction." –Tolstoy

Simplifying Fractions

Helpful		**Example:**
	– Evenly divide both the top and bottom of the fraction by 2, 3, 5, 7, ... etc.	
Hints	– Continue until you can't go any further.	$\dfrac{4}{12} = \dfrac{2}{6} = \dfrac{1}{3}$

✎ *Simplify the fractions.*

1) $\dfrac{22}{36} = 11$

2) $\dfrac{8}{10}$

3) $\dfrac{12}{18}$

4) $\dfrac{6}{8}$

5) $\dfrac{13}{39}$

6) $\dfrac{5}{20}$

7) $\dfrac{16}{36}$

8) $\dfrac{18}{36}$

9) $\dfrac{20}{50}$

10) $\dfrac{6}{54}$

11) $\dfrac{45}{81}$

12) $\dfrac{21}{28}$

13) $\dfrac{35}{56}$

14) $\dfrac{52}{64}$

15) $\dfrac{13}{65}$

16) $\dfrac{44}{77}$

17) $\dfrac{21}{42}$

18) $\dfrac{15}{36}$

19) $\dfrac{9}{24}$

20) $\dfrac{20}{80}$

21) $\dfrac{25}{45}$

Adding and Subtracting Fractions

Helpful

Hints

- For "like" fractions (fractions with the same denominator), add or subtract the numerators and write the answer over the common denominator.
- Find equivalent fractions with the same denominator before you can add or subtract fractions with different denominators.
- Adding and Subtracting with the same denominator:

$$\frac{a}{b} + \frac{c}{b} = \frac{a+c}{b}$$
$$\frac{a}{b} - \frac{c}{b} = \frac{a-c}{b}$$

- Adding and Subtracting fractions with different denominators:

$$\frac{a}{b} + \frac{c}{d} = \frac{ad+cb}{bd}$$
$$\frac{a}{b} - \frac{c}{d} = \frac{ad-cb}{bd}$$

✎ Add fractions.

1) $\frac{2}{3} + \frac{1}{2}$ $\frac{7}{6}$

2) $\frac{3}{5} + \frac{1}{3}$ $\frac{14}{15}$

3) $\frac{5}{6} + \frac{1}{2}$

4) $\frac{7}{4} + \frac{5}{9}$ $\frac{83}{36}$

5) $\frac{2}{5} + \frac{1}{5}$ $\frac{15}{25}$ $\frac{3}{5}$

6) $\frac{3}{7} + \frac{1}{2}$ $\frac{13}{14}$

7) $\frac{3}{4} + \frac{2}{5}$ $= \frac{23}{20}$

8) $\frac{2}{3} + \frac{1}{5}$ $\frac{13}{15}$

9) $\frac{16}{25} + \frac{3}{5}$

✎ Subtract fractions.

10) $\frac{4}{5} - \frac{2}{5}$

11) $\frac{3}{5} - \frac{2}{7}$

12) $\frac{1}{2} - \frac{1}{3}$

13) $\frac{8}{9} - \frac{3}{5}$

14) $\frac{3}{7} - \frac{3}{14}$

15) $\frac{4}{15} - \frac{1}{10}$

16) $\frac{3}{4} - \frac{13}{18}$

17) $\frac{5}{8} - \frac{2}{5}$

18) $\frac{1}{2} - \frac{1}{9}$

Multiplying and Dividing Fractions

Helpful Hints	– **Multiplying fractions:** multiply the top numbers and multiply the bottom numbers. – **Dividing fractions:** Keep, Change, Flip Keep first fraction, change division sign to multiplication, and flip the numerator and denominator of the second fraction. Then, solve!	Example: $\dfrac{a}{b} \times \dfrac{c}{d} = \dfrac{a \times c}{b \times d}$ $\dfrac{a}{b} \div \dfrac{c}{d} = \dfrac{a}{b} \times \dfrac{d}{c} = \dfrac{ad}{bc}$

✍ Multiplying fractions. Then simplify.

1) $\dfrac{1}{5} \times \dfrac{2}{3}$

2) $\dfrac{3}{4} \times \dfrac{2}{3}$

3) $\dfrac{2}{5} \times \dfrac{3}{7}$

4) $\dfrac{3}{8} \times \dfrac{1}{3}$

5) $\dfrac{3}{5} \times \dfrac{2}{5}$

6) $\dfrac{7}{9} \times \dfrac{1}{3}$

7) $\dfrac{2}{3} \times \dfrac{3}{8}$

8) $\dfrac{1}{4} \times \dfrac{1}{3}$

9) $\dfrac{5}{7} \times \dfrac{7}{12}$

✍ Dividing fractions.

10) $\dfrac{2}{9} \div \dfrac{1}{4}$

11) $\dfrac{1}{2} \div \dfrac{1}{3}$

12) $\dfrac{6}{11} \div \dfrac{3}{4}$

13) $\dfrac{11}{14} \div \dfrac{1}{10}$

14) $\dfrac{3}{5} \div \dfrac{5}{9}$

15) $\dfrac{1}{2} \div \dfrac{1}{2}$

16) $\dfrac{3}{5} \div \dfrac{1}{5}$

17) $\dfrac{12}{21} \div \dfrac{3}{7}$

18) $\dfrac{5}{14} \div \dfrac{9}{10}$

Adding Mixed Numbers

Helpful	Use the following steps for both adding and subtracting mixed numbers.	**Example:**
Hints	– Find the Least Common Denominator (LCD) – Find the equivalent fractions for each mixed number. – Add fractions after finding common denominator. – Write your answer in lowest terms.	$1\frac{3}{4} + 2\frac{3}{8} = 4\frac{1}{8}$

✎**Add.**

1) $4\frac{1}{2} + 5\frac{1}{2}$

2) $2\frac{3}{8} + 3\frac{1}{8}$

3) $6\frac{1}{5} + 3\frac{2}{5}$

4) $1\frac{1}{3} + 2\frac{2}{3}$

5) $5\frac{1}{6} + 5\frac{1}{2}$

6) $3\frac{1}{3} + 1\frac{1}{3}$

7) $1\frac{10}{11} + 1\frac{1}{3}$

8) $2\frac{3}{6} + 1\frac{1}{2}$

9) $5\frac{3}{5} + 5\frac{1}{5}$

10) $7 + \frac{1}{5}$

11) $1\frac{5}{7} + \frac{1}{3}$

12) $2\frac{1}{4} + 1\frac{1}{2}$

Subtract Mixed Numbers

Helpful

Hints

Use the following steps for both adding and subtracting mixed numbers.

Find the Least Common Denominator (LCD)
- Find the equivalent fractions for each mixed number.
- Add or subtract fractions after finding common denominator.
- Write your answer in lowest terms.

Example:

$$5\frac{2}{3} - 3\frac{2}{7} = 2\frac{8}{21}$$

✎ *Subtract.*

1) $4\frac{1}{2} - 3\frac{1}{2}$

2) $3\frac{3}{8} - 3\frac{1}{8}$

3) $6\frac{3}{5} - 5\frac{1}{5}$

4) $2\frac{1}{3} - 1\frac{2}{3}$

5) $6\frac{1}{6} - 5\frac{1}{2}$

6) $3\frac{1}{3} - 1\frac{1}{3}$

7) $2\frac{10}{11} - 1\frac{1}{3}$

8) $2\frac{1}{2} - 1\frac{1}{2}$

9) $6\frac{3}{5} - 2\frac{1}{5}$

10) $7\frac{2}{5} - 1\frac{1}{5}$

11) $2\frac{5}{7} - 1\frac{1}{3}$

12) $2\frac{1}{4} - 1\frac{1}{2}$

Multiplying Mixed Numbers

Helpful	1- Convert the mixed numbers to improper fractions.	**Example:**

1- Convert the mixed numbers to improper fractions.

2- Multiply fractions and simplify if necessary.

$$a\frac{c}{b} = a + \frac{c}{b} = \frac{ab+c}{b}$$

Example:

$$2\frac{1}{3} \times 5\frac{3}{7} =$$

$$\frac{7}{3} \times \frac{38}{7} = \frac{38}{3} = 12\frac{2}{3}$$

Helpful Hints

✎ **Find each product.**

1) $1\frac{2}{3} \times 1\frac{1}{4}$

2) $1\frac{3}{5} \times 1\frac{2}{3}$

3) $1\frac{2}{3} \times 3\frac{2}{7}$

4) $4\frac{1}{8} \times 1\frac{2}{5}$

5) $2\frac{2}{5} \times 3\frac{1}{5}$

6) $1\frac{1}{3} \times 1\frac{2}{3}$

7) $1\frac{5}{8} \times 2\frac{1}{2}$

8) $3\frac{2}{5} \times 2\frac{1}{5}$

9) $2\frac{2}{3} \times 4\frac{1}{4}$

10) $2\frac{3}{5} \times 1\frac{2}{4}$

11) $1\frac{1}{3} \times 1\frac{1}{4}$

12) $3\frac{2}{5} \times 1\frac{1}{5}$

Dividing Mixed Numbers

Helpful	1- Convert the mixed numbers to improper fractions.	**Example:**
Hints	2- Divide fractions and simplify if necessary.	$10\frac{1}{2} \div 5\frac{3}{5} =$

$$a\frac{c}{b} = a + \frac{c}{b} = \frac{ab+c}{b}$$

$$\frac{21}{2} \div \frac{28}{5} = \frac{21}{2} \times \frac{5}{28} = \frac{105}{56}$$

$$= 1\frac{7}{8}$$

✏️ *Find each quotient.*

1) $2\frac{1}{5} \div 2\frac{1}{2}$

2) $2\frac{3}{5} \div 1\frac{1}{3}$

3) $3\frac{1}{6} \div 4\frac{2}{3}$

4) $1\frac{2}{3} \div 3\frac{1}{3}$

5) $4\frac{1}{8} \div 2\frac{2}{4}$

6) $3\frac{1}{2} \div 2\frac{3}{5}$

7) $3\frac{5}{9} \div 1\frac{2}{5}$

8) $2\frac{2}{7} \div 1\frac{1}{2}$

9) $3\frac{1}{5} \div 1\frac{1}{2}$

10) $4\frac{3}{5} \div 2\frac{1}{3}$

11) $6\frac{1}{6} \div 1\frac{2}{3}$

12) $2\frac{2}{3} \div 1\frac{1}{3}$

Comparing Decimals

Helpful	-	**Decimals:** is a fraction written in a special form. For example, instead of writing $\frac{1}{2}$ you can write 0.5.	**Example:**
Hints	-	**For comparing:** Equal to = Less than < greater than > greater than or equal ≥ Less than or equal ≤	2.67 > 0.267

✏️ *Write the correct comparison symbol (>, < or =).*

1) 1.25 2.3	9) 8 0.8	17) 5.52 0.552
2) 0.5 0.23	10) 4.56 0.456	18) 0.33 0.033
3) 3.2 3.2	11) 1.12 1.14	19) 14.4 14.4
4) 4.58 45.8	12) 2.77 2.78	20) 0.05 0.50
5) 2.75 0.275	13) 6.08 6.11	21) 0.59 0.7
6) 5.2 5	14) 1.11 0.211	22) 0.5 0.05
7) 3.1 0.31	15) 2.6 2.55	23) 0.90 0.9
8) 6.33 0.733	16) 1.24 1.25	24) 0.27 0.4

Rounding Decimals

Helpful **Hints**	We can round decimals to a certain accuracy or number of decimal places. This is used to make calculation easier to do and results easier to understand, when exact values are not too important.	**Example:**

First, you'll need to remember your place values:

$\underline{6}.37 = 6$

12.4567

1: tens   2: ones   4: tenths

5: hundredths   6: thousandths   7: tens thousandths

✍ **Round each decimal number to the nearest place indicated.**

1) 0.2$\underline{3}$

2) 4.$\underline{0}$4

3) 5.$\underline{6}$23

4) 0.2$\underline{6}$6

5) $\underline{6}$.37

6) 0.8$\underline{8}$

7) 8.2$\underline{4}$

8) $\underline{7}$.0760

9) 1.6$\underline{2}$9

10) 6.$\underline{3}$959

11) $\underline{1}$.9

12) $\underline{5}$.2167

13) 5.$\underline{8}$63

14) 8.$\underline{5}$4

15) 8$\underline{0}$.69

16) 6$\underline{5}$.85

17) 70.7$\underline{8}$

18) 61$\underline{5}$.755

19) 1$\underline{6}$.4

20) 9$\underline{5}$.81

21) $\underline{2}$.408

22) 7$\underline{6}$.3

23) 116.$\underline{5}$14

24) 8.$\underline{0}$6

Adding and Subtracting Decimals

Helpful	1– Line up the numbers.	Example:
	2– Add zeros to have same number of digits for both numbers.	
Hints		16.18
	3– Add or Subtract using column addition or subtraction.	$\underline{-\ 13.45}$
		2.73

✎ **Add and subtract decimals.**

1) $\begin{array}{r} 15.14 \\ -\ 12.18 \\ \hline \end{array}$

3) $\begin{array}{r} 82.56 \\ +\ 12.28 \\ \hline \end{array}$

5) $\begin{array}{r} 90.37 \\ +\ 56.97 \\ \hline \end{array}$

2) $\begin{array}{r} 65.72 \\ +\ 43.67 \\ \hline \end{array}$

4) $\begin{array}{r} 34.18 \\ -\ 23.45 \\ \hline \end{array}$

6) $\begin{array}{r} 45.78 \\ -\ 23.39 \\ \hline \end{array}$

✎ **Solve.**

7) _____ $+ 1.3 = 4.8$

10) $6.9 +$ _____ $= 16.4$

8) $4.2 +$ _____ $= 11.6$

11) _____ $+ 5.1 = 8.6$

9) $9.9 +$ _____ $= 16$

12) _____ $+ 7.9 = 15.2$

Multiplying and Dividing Decimals

Helpful *Hints*	**For Multiplication:** – Set up and multiply the numbers as you do with whole numbers. – Count the total number of decimal places in both of the factors. – Place the decimal point in the product. **For Division:** – If the divisor is not a whole number, move decimal point to right to make it a whole number. Do the same for dividend. – Divide similar to whole numbers.

✎ *Find each product.*

1) $\begin{array}{r} 4.5 \\ \times\ 1.6 \\ \hline \end{array}$

2) $\begin{array}{r} 7.7 \\ \times\ 9.9 \\ \hline \end{array}$

3) $\begin{array}{r} 2.6 \\ \times\ 1.5 \\ \hline \end{array}$

4) $\begin{array}{r} 8.9 \\ \times\ 9.7 \\ \hline \end{array}$

5) $\begin{array}{r} 15.1 \\ \times\ 12.6 \\ \hline \end{array}$

6) $\begin{array}{r} 6.9 \\ \times\ 3.3 \\ \hline \end{array}$

7) $\begin{array}{r} 5.7 \\ \times\ 7.8 \\ \hline \end{array}$

8) $\begin{array}{r} 98.20 \\ \times\ 100 \\ \hline \end{array}$

9) $\begin{array}{r} 23.99 \\ \times\ 1000 \\ \hline \end{array}$

✎ *Find each quotient.*

10) $9.2 \div 3.6$

11) $27.6 \div 3.8$

12) $12.6 \div 4.7$

13) $6.5 \div 8.1$

14) $1.4 \div 10$

15) $3.6 \div 100$

16) $4.24 \div 10$

17) $14.6 \div 100$

18) $1.8 \div 1000$

Converting Between Fractions, Decimals and Mixed Numbers

Helpful *Hints*	**Fraction to Decimal:**
	− Divide the top number by the bottom number.
	Decimal to Fraction:
	− Write decimal over 1.
	− Multiply both top and bottom by 10 for every digit on the right side of the decimal point.
	− Simplify.

✍ *Convert fractions to decimals.*

1) $\dfrac{9}{10}$

4) $\dfrac{2}{5}$

7) $\dfrac{12}{10}$

2) $\dfrac{56}{100}$

5) $\dfrac{3}{9}$

8) $\dfrac{8}{5}$

3) $\dfrac{3}{4}$

6) $\dfrac{40}{50}$

9) $\dfrac{69}{10}$

✍ *Convert decimal into fraction or mixed numbers.*

10) 0.3

14) 0.8

18) 0.08

11) 4.5

15) 0.25

19) 0.45

12) 2.5

16) 0.14

20) 2.6

13) 2.3

17) 0.2

21) 5.2

Factoring Numbers

Helpful	-	Factoring numbers means to break the numbers into their prime factors.	**Example:**
Hints	-	First few prime numbers: 2, 3, 5, 7, 11, 13, 17, 19	$12 = 2 \times 2 \times 3$

✍ List all positive factors of each number.

1) 68   6) 78   11) 54

2) 56   7) 50   12) 28

3) 24   8) 98   13) 55

4) 40   9) 45   14) 85

5) 86   10) 26   15) 48

✍ List the prime factorization for each number.

16) 50   19) 21   22) 26

17) 25   20) 45   23) 86

18) 69   21) 68   24) 93

Greatest Common Factor

Helpful	- List the prime factors of each number. - Multiply common prime factors.	**Example:** $200 = 2 \times 2 \times 2 \times 5 \times 5$ $60 = 2 \times 2 \times 3 \times 5$ GCF $(200, 60) = 2 \times 2 \times 5 = 20$
Hints		

✎ *Find the GCF for each number pair.*

1) 20, 30

2) 4, 14

3) 5, 45

4) 68, 12

5) 5, 12

6) 15, 27

7) 3, 24

8) 34, 6

9) 4, 10

10) 5, 3

11) 6, 16

12) 30, 3

13) 24, 28

14) 70, 10

15) 45, 8

16) 90, 35

17) 78, 34

18) 55, 75

19) 60, 72

20) 100, 78

21) 30, 40

Least Common Multiple

Helpful *Hints*	- Find the GCF for the two numbers. - Divide that GCF into either number. - Take that answer and multiply it by the other number.	**Example:** LCM (200, 60): GCF is 20 $200 \div 20 = 10$ $10 \times 60 = 600$

✎ **Find the LCM for each number pair.**

1) 4, 14

2) 5, 15

3) 16, 10

4) 4, 34

5) 8, 3

6) 12, 24

7) 9, 18

8) 5, 6

9) 8, 19

10) 9, 21

11) 19, 29

12) 7, 6

13) 25, 6

14) 4, 8

15) 30, 10, 50

16) 18, 36, 27

17) 12, 8, 18

18) 8, 18, 4

19) 26, 20, 30

20) 10, 4, 24

21) 15, 30, 45

Answers of Worksheets – Chapter 1

Simplifying Fractions

1) $\dfrac{11}{18}$

2) $\dfrac{4}{5}$

3) $\dfrac{2}{3}$

4) $\dfrac{3}{4}$

5) $\dfrac{1}{3}$

6) $\dfrac{1}{4}$

7) $\dfrac{4}{9}$

8) $\dfrac{1}{2}$

9) $\dfrac{2}{5}$

10) $\dfrac{1}{9}$

11) $\dfrac{5}{9}$

12) $\dfrac{3}{4}$

13) $\dfrac{5}{8}$

14) $\dfrac{13}{16}$

15) $\dfrac{1}{5}$

16) $\dfrac{4}{7}$

17) $\dfrac{1}{2}$

18) $\dfrac{5}{12}$

19) $\dfrac{3}{8}$

20) $\dfrac{1}{4}$

21) $\dfrac{5}{9}$

Adding and Subtracting Fractions

1) $\dfrac{7}{6}$

2) $\dfrac{14}{15}$

3) $\dfrac{4}{3}$

4) $\dfrac{83}{36}$

5) $\dfrac{3}{5}$

6) $\dfrac{13}{14}$

7) $\dfrac{23}{20}$

8) $\dfrac{13}{15}$

9) $\dfrac{31}{25}$

10) $\dfrac{2}{5}$

11) $\dfrac{11}{35}$

12) $\dfrac{1}{6}$

13) $\dfrac{13}{45}$

14) $\dfrac{3}{14}$

15) $\dfrac{1}{6}$

16) $\dfrac{1}{36}$

17) $\dfrac{9}{40}$

18) $\dfrac{7}{18}$

Multiplying and Dividing Fractions

1) $\dfrac{2}{15}$

2) $\dfrac{1}{2}$

3) $\dfrac{6}{35}$

4) $\dfrac{1}{8}$

5) $\dfrac{6}{25}$

6) $\dfrac{7}{27}$

7) $\dfrac{1}{4}$

8) $\dfrac{1}{12}$

9) $\dfrac{5}{12}$

10) $\dfrac{8}{9}$

11) $\dfrac{3}{2}$

12) $\dfrac{8}{11}$

13) $\dfrac{55}{7}$

14) $\dfrac{27}{25}$

15) 1

16) 3

17) $\dfrac{4}{3}$

18) $\dfrac{25}{63}$

Adding Mixed Numbers

1) 10

2) $5\dfrac{1}{2}$

3) $9\dfrac{3}{5}$

4) 4

5) $10\dfrac{2}{3}$

6) $4\dfrac{2}{3}$

7) $3\dfrac{8}{33}$

8) 4

9) $10\dfrac{4}{5}$

10) $7\dfrac{1}{5}$

11) $2\dfrac{1}{21}$

12) $3\dfrac{3}{4}$

Subtract Mixed Numbers

1) 1

2) $\dfrac{1}{4}$

3) $1\dfrac{2}{5}$

4) $\dfrac{2}{3}$

5) $\dfrac{2}{3}$

6) 2

7) $1\dfrac{19}{33}$

8) 1

9) $4\dfrac{2}{5}$

10) $6\dfrac{1}{5}$

11) $1\dfrac{8}{21}$

12) $\dfrac{3}{4}$

Multiplying Mixed Numbers

1) $2\frac{1}{12}$

2) $2\frac{2}{3}$

3) $5\frac{10}{21}$

4) $5\frac{31}{40}$

5) $7\frac{17}{25}$

6) $2\frac{2}{9}$

7) $4\frac{1}{16}$

8) $7\frac{12}{25}$

9) $11\frac{1}{3}$

10) $3\frac{9}{10}$

11) $1\frac{2}{3}$

12) $4\frac{2}{25}$

Dividing Mixed Numbers

1) $\frac{22}{25}$

2) $1\frac{19}{20}$

3) $\frac{19}{28}$

4) $\frac{1}{2}$

5) $1\frac{13}{20}$

6) $1\frac{9}{26}$

7) $2\frac{34}{63}$

8) $1\frac{11}{21}$

9) $2\frac{2}{15}$

10) $1\frac{34}{35}$

11) $3\frac{7}{10}$

12) 2

Comparing Decimals

1) $1.25 < 2.3$

2) $0.5 > 0.23$

3) $3.2 = 3.2$

4) $4.58 < 45.8$

5) $2.75 > 0.275$

6) $5.2 > 5$

7) $3.1 > 0.31$

8) $6.33 > 0.733$

9) $8 > 0.8$

10) $4.56 > 0.456$

11) $1.12 < 1.14$

12) $2.77 < 2.78$

13) $6.08 < 6.11$

14) $1.11 > 0.211$

15) $2.6 > 2.55$

16) $1.24 < 1.25$

17) $5.52 > 0.552$

18) $0.33 > 0.033$

19) $14.4 = 14.4$

20) $0.05 < 0.50$

21) $0.59 < 0.7$

22) $0.5 > 0.05$

23) $0.90 = 0.9$

24) $0.27 < 0.4$

Rounding Decimals

1) 0.2	9) 1.63	17) 70.8
2) 4.0	10) 6.4	18) 616
3) 5.6	11) 2	19) 16
4) 0.3	12) 5	20) 96
5) 6	13) 5.9	21) 2
6) 0.9	14) 8.5	22) 76
7) 8.2	15) 81	23) 116.5
8) 7	16) 66	24) 8.1

Adding and Subtracting Decimals

1) 2.96	5) 147.34	9) 6.1
2) 109.39	6) 22.39	10) 9.5
3) 94.84	7) 3.5	11) 3.5
4) 10.73	8) 7.4	12) 7.3

Multiplying and Dividing Decimals

1) 7.2	7) 44.46	13) 0.8024…
2) 76.23	8) 9820	14) 0.14
3) 3.9	9) 23990	15) 0.036
4) 86.33	10) 2.5555…	16) 0.424
5) 190.26	11) 7.2631…	17) 0.146
6) 22.77	12) 2.6808…	18) 0.0018

Converting Between Fractions, Decimals and Mixed Numbers

1) 0.9	7) 1.2	12) $2\frac{1}{2}$
2) 0.56	8) 1.6	13) $2\frac{3}{10}$
3) 0.75	9) 6.9	14) $\frac{4}{5}$
4) 0.4	10) $\frac{3}{10}$	15) $\frac{1}{4}$
5) 0.333…	11) $4\frac{1}{2}$	
6) 0.8		

16) $\frac{7}{50}$ 18) $\frac{2}{25}$ 20) $2\frac{3}{5}$

17) $\frac{1}{5}$ 19) $\frac{9}{20}$ 21) $5\frac{1}{5}$

Factoring Numbers

1) 1, 2, 4, 17, 34, 68
2) 1, 2, 4, 7, 8, 14, 28, 56
3) 1, 2, 3, 4, 6, 8, 12, 24
4) 1, 2, 4, 5, 8, 10, 20, 40
5) 1, 2, 43, 86
6) 1, 2, 3, 6, 13, 26, 39, 78
7) 1, 2, 5, 10, 25, 50
8) 1, 2, 7, 14, 49, 98
9) 1, 3, 5, 9, 15, 45
10) 1, 2, 13, 26
11) 1, 2, 3, 6, 9, 18, 27, 54
12) 1, 2, 4, 7, 14, 28

13) 1, 5, 11, 55
14) 1, 5, 17, 85
15) 1, 2, 3, 4, 6, 8, 12, 16, 24, 48
16) $2 \times 5 \times 5$
17) 5×5
18) 3×23
19) 3×7
20) $3 \times 3 \times 5$
21) $2 \times 2 \times 17$
22) 2×13
23) 2×43
24) 3×31

Greatest Common Factor

1) 10
2) 2
3) 5
4) 4
5) 1
6) 3
7) 3

8) 2
9) 2
10) 1
11) 2
12) 3
13) 4
14) 10

15) 1
16) 5
17) 2
18) 5
19) 12
20) 2
21) 10

Least Common Multiple

1) 28
2) 15
3) 80
4) 68
5) 24
6) 24
7) 18

8) 30
9) 152
10) 63
11) 551
12) 42
13) 150
14) 8

15) 150
16) 108
17) 72
18) 72
19) 780
20) 120
21) 90

Chapter 2: Real Numbers and Integers

Topics that you'll learn in this chapter:

- ✓ Adding and Subtracting Integers
- ✓ Multiplying and Dividing Integers
- ✓ Ordering Integers and Numbers
- ✓ Arrange and Order, Comparing Integers
- ✓ Order of Operations
- ✓ Mixed Integer Computations
- ✓ Integers and Absolute Value

"Wherever there is number, there is beauty." –Proclus

Adding and Subtracting Integers

Helpful		Integers: {... , −3, −2, −1, 0, 1, 2, 3, ...}	Example:
	-	Includes: zero, counting numbers, and the negative of the counting numbers.	
Hints			$12 + 10 = 22$
		− Add a positive integer by moving to the right on the number line.	$25 − 13 = 12$
			$(−24) + 12 = −12$
		− Add a negative integer by moving to the left on the number line.	$(−14) + (−12) = −26$
		− Subtract an integer by adding its opposite.	$14 − (−13) = 27$

✍ Find the sum.

1) $(− 12) + (− 4)$

2) $5 + (− 24)$

3) $(− 14) + 23$

4) $(− 8) + (39)$

5) $43 + (−12)$

6) $(− 23) + (− 4) + 3$

7) $4 + (− 12) + (− 10) + (− 25)$

8) $19 + (− 15) + 25 + 11$

9) $(− 9) + (− 12) + (32 − 14)$

10) $4 + (− 30) + (45 − 34)$

✍ Find the difference.

11) $(− 14) − (− 9) − (18)$

12) $(− 9) − (− 25)$

13) $(− 12) − (8)$

14) $(28) − (− 4)$

15) $(34) − (2)$

16) $(55) − (− 5) + (− 4)$

17) $(9) − (2) − (− 5)$

18) $(2) − (4) − (− 15)$

19) $(23) − (4) − (− 34)$

20) $(− 45) − (− 87)$

Multiplying and Dividing Integers

Helpful	(negative) × (negative) = positive	**Examples:**
	(negative) ÷ (negative) = positive	$3 \times 2 = 6$
Hints	(negative) × (positive) = negative	$3 \times -3 = -9$
	(negative) ÷ (positive) = negative	$-2 \times -2 = 4$
	(positive) × (positive) = positive	$10 \div 2 = 5$
		$-4 \div 2 = -2$
		$-12 \div -6 = 3$

✎ **Find each product.**

1) $(-8) \times (-2)$

2) 3×6

3) $(-4) \times 5 \times (-6)$

4) $2 \times (-6) \times (-6)$

5) $11 \times (-12)$

6) $10 \times (-5)$

7) 8×8

8) $(-8) \times (-9)$

9) $6 \times (-5) \times 3$

10) $6 \times (-1) \times 2$

✎ **Find each quotient.**

11) $18 \div 3$

12) $(-24) \div 4$

13) $(-63) \div (-9)$

14) $54 \div 9$

15) $20 \div (-2)$

16) $(-66) \div (-11)$

17) $64 \div 8$

18) $(-121) \div 11$

19) $72 \div 9$

20) $16 \div 4$

Ordering Integers and Numbers

Helpful *Hints*	To compare numbers, you can use number line! As you move from left to right on the number line, you find a bigger number!	**Example:** Order integers from least to greatest. $(-11, -13, 7, -2, 12)$ $-13 < -11 < -2 < 7 < 12$

✍ **Order each set of integers from least to greatest.**

1) $-15, -19, 20, -4, 1$ ___, ___, ___, ___, ___, ___

2) $6, -5, 4, -3, 2$ ___, ___, ___, ___, ___, ___

3) $15, -42, 19, 0, -22$ ___, ___, ___, ___, ___, ___

4) $26, -91, 0, -13, 67, -55$ ___, ___, ___, ___, ___, ___

5) $-17, -71, 90, -25, -54, -39$ ___, ___, ___, ___, ___, ___

6) $98, 5, 46, 19, 77, 24$ ___, ___, ___, ___, ___, ___

✍ **Order each set of integers from greatest to least.**

7) $-2, 5, -3, 6, -4$ ___, ___, ___, ___, ___, ___

8) $-37, 7, -17, 27, 47$ ___, ___, ___, ___, ___, ___

9) $32, -27, 19, -17, 15$ ___, ___, ___, ___, ___, ___

10) $68, 81, 21, -18, 94, 72$ ___, ___, ___, ___, ___, ___

Arrange, Order, and Comparing Integers

Helpful *Hints*	When using a number line, numbers increase as you move to the right.	**Examples:** $5 < 7,$ $-5 < -2$ $-18 < -12$

✍ *Arrange these integers in descending order.*

1) 21, 71, − 18, − 10, 82   ___, ___, ___, ___, ___, ___

2) 15, 11, 20, 12, − 9, − 5   ___, ___, ___, ___, ___, ___

3) − 5, 20, 15, 9, −11   ___, ___, ___, ___, ___, ___

4) 19, 18, − 9, − 6, − 11   ___, ___, ___, ___, ___, ___

5) 56, − 34, − 12, − 5, 32   ___, ___, ___, ___, ___, ___

✍ *Compare. Use >, =, <*

6) − 8 ____ 12

7) − 10 ____ −16

8) 43 ____ 34

9) 15 ____ −16

10) − 354 ____ −345

11) − 56 ____ − 58

12) 78 ____ 87

13) − 92 ____ − 102

14) − 12 ____ − 12

15) − 721 ____ − 821

Order of Operations

Helpful	-	Use "order of operations" rule when there are more than one math operation.	**Example:**
Hints	-	PEMDAS (parentheses / exponents / multiply / divide / add / subtract)	$(12 + 4) \div (-4) = -4$

✎**Evaluate each expression.**

1) $(2 \times 2) + 5$

2) $24 - (3 \times 3)$

3) $(6 \times 4) + 8$

4) $25 - (4 \times 2)$

5) $(6 \times 5) + 3$

6) $64 - (2 \times 4)$

7) $25 + (1 \times 8)$

8) $(6 \times 7) + 7$

9) $48 \div (4 + 4)$

10) $(7 + 11) \div (-2)$

11) $9 + (2 \times 5) + 10$

12) $(5 + 8) \times \dfrac{3}{5} + 2$

13) $2 \times 7 - \left(\dfrac{10}{9 - 4}\right)$

14) $(12 + 2 - 5) \times 7 - 1$

15) $\left(\dfrac{7}{5 - 1}\right) \times (2 + 6) \times 2$

16) $20 \div (4 - (10 - 8))$

17) $\dfrac{50}{4\,(5 - 4) - 3}$

18) $2 + (8 \times 2)$

Mixed Integer Computations

Helpful *Hints*	**It worth remembering:**	**Example:**
	(negative) × (negative) = positive	
	(negative) ÷ (negative) = positive	$(-5) + 6 = 1$
	(negative) × (positive) = negative	$(-3) \times (-2) = 6$
	(negative) ÷ (positive) = negative	$(9) \div (-3) = -3$
	(positive) × (positive) = positive	

✎*Compute.*

1) $(-70) \div (-5)$

2) $(-14) \times 3$

3) $(-4) \times (-15)$

4) $(-65) \div 5$

5) $18 \times (-7)$

6) $(-12) \times (-2)$

7) $\dfrac{(-60)}{(-20)}$

8) $24 \div (-8)$

9) $22 \div (-11)$

10) $\dfrac{(-27)}{3}$

11) $4 \times (-4)$

12) $\dfrac{(-48)}{12}$

13) $(-14) \times (-2)$

14) $(-7) \times (7)$

15) $\dfrac{-30}{-6}$

16) $(-54) \div 6$

17) $(-60) \div (-5)$

18) $(-7) \times (-12)$

19) $(-14) \times 5$

20) $88 \div (-8)$

Integers and Absolute Value

Helpful	To find an absolute value of a number, just find it's distance from 0!	**Example:**
Hints		$\|-6\| = 6$
		$\|6\| = 6$
		$\|-12\| = 12$
		$\|12\| = 12$

✍ **Write absolute value of each number.**

1) -4

2) -7

3) -8

4) 4

5) 5

6) -10

7) 1

8) 6

9) 8

10) -2

11) -1

12) 10

13) 3

14) 7

15) -5

16) -3

17) -9

18) 2

19) 4

20) -6

21) 9

✍ *Evaluate.*

22) $\|-43\| - \|12\| + 10$

23) $76 + \|-15 - 45\| - \|3\|$

24) $30 + \|-62\| - 46$

25) $\|32\| - \|-78\| + 90$

26) $\|-35 + 4\| + 6 - 4$

27) $\|-4\| + \|-11\|$

28) $\|-6 + 3 - 4\| + \|7 + 7\|$

29) $\|-9\| + \|-19\| - 5$

Answers of Worksheets – CHAPTER 2

Adding and Subtracting Integers

1) − 16	8) 40	15) 32
2) − 19	9) − 3	16) 56
3) 9	10) − 15	17) 12
4) 31	11) − 23	18) 13
5) 31	12) 16	19) 53
6) − 24	13) − 20	20) 42
7) − 43	14) 32	

Multiplying and Dividing Integers

1) 16	8) 72	15) − 10
2) 18	9) − 90	16) 6
3) 120	10) − 12	17) 8
4) 72	11) 6	18) − 11
5) − 132	12) − 6	19) 8
6) − 50	13) 7	20) 4
7) 64	14) 6	

Ordering Integers and Numbers

1) − 19, − 15, − 4, 1, 20	6) 5, 19, 24, 46, 77, 98
2) − 5, − 3, 2, 4, 6	7) 6, 5, − 2, − 3, − 4
3) − 42, − 22, 0, 15, 19	8) 47, 27, 7, − 17, − 37
4) − 91, − 55, − 13, 0, 26, 67	9) 32, 19, 15, − 17, − 27
5) − 71, − 54, − 39, − 25, − 17, 90	10) 94, 81, 72, 68, 21, − 18

Arrange and Order, Comparing Integers

1) 82, 71, 21, − 10, − 18

2) 20, 15, 12, 11, − 5, − 9

3) 20, 15, 9, − 5, −11

4) 19, 18, − 6, − 9, − 11

5) 56, 32, − 5, − 12, − 34

6) <	10) <	14) =
7) >	11) >	15) >
8) >	12) <	
9) >	13) >	

Order of Operations

1) 9	7) 33	13) 12
2) 15	8) 49	14) 62
3) 32	9) 6	15) 28
4) 17	10) − 9	16) 10
5) 33	11) 29	17) 50
6) 56	12) 9.8	18) 18

Mixed Integer Computations

1) 14	8) − 3	15) 5
2) − 42	9) − 2	16) − 9
3) 60	10) − 9	17) 12
4) − 13	11) − 16	18) 84
5) − 126	12) − 4	19) − 70
6) 24	13) 28	20) − 11
7) 3	14) − 49	

Integers and Absolute Value

1) 4	11) 1	21) 9
2) 7	12) 10	22) 41
3) 8	13) 3	23) 133
4) 4	14) 7	24) 46
5) 5	15) 5	25) 44
6) 10	16) 3	26) 33
7) 1	17) 9	27) 15
8) 6	18) 2	28) 21
9) 8	19) 4	29) 23
10) 2	20) 6	

Chapter 3: Proportions and Ratios

Topics that you'll learn in this chapter:

- ✓ Writing Ratios
- ✓ Simplifying Ratios
- ✓ Create a Proportion
- ✓ Similar Figures
- ✓ Simple Interest
- ✓ Ratio and Rates Word Problems

"Do not worry about your difficulties in mathematics. I can assure you mine are still greater." – Albert Einstein

Writing Ratios

| *Helpful* | – A ratio is a comparison of two numbers. Ratio can be written as a division. | **Example:** |
| *Hints* | | $3 : 5$, or $\dfrac{3}{5}$ |

✍ Express each ratio as a rate and unite rate.

1) 120 miles on 4 gallons of gas.

2) 24 dollars for 6 books.

3) 200 miles on 14 gallons of gas

4) 24 inches of snow in 8 hours

✍ Express each ratio as a fraction in the simplest form.

5) 3 feet out of 30 feet

6) 18 cakes out of 42 cakes

7) 16 dimes t0 24 dimes

8) 12 dimes out of 48 coins

9) 14 cups to 84 cups

10) 45 gallons to 65 gallons

11) 10 miles out of 40 miles

12) 22 blue cars out of 55 cars

13) 32 pennies to 300 pennies

14) 24 beetles out of 86 insects

Simplifying Ratios

Helpful	– You can calculate equivalent ratios by multiplying or dividing both sides of the ratio by the same number.	**Examples:**
Hints		3 : 6 = 1 : 2
		4 : 9 = 8 : 18

✎ *Reduce each ratio.*

1) 21 : 49

2) 20 : 40

3) 10 : 50

4) 14 : 18

5) 45 : 27

6) 49 : 21

7) 100 : 10

8) 12 : 8

9) 35 : 45

10) 8 : 20

11) 25 : 35

12) 21 : 27

13) 52 : 82

14) 12 : 36

15) 24 : 3

16) 15 : 30

17) 3 : 36

18) 8 : 16

19) 6 : 100

20) 2 : 20

21) 10 : 60

22) 14 : 63

23) 68 : 80

24) 8 : 80

Create a Proportion

Helpful	– A proportion contains 2 equal fractions! A proportion simply means that two fractions are equal.	**Example:**
Hints		2, 4, 8, 16
		$\dfrac{2}{4} = \dfrac{8}{16}$

✎ *Create proportion from the given set of numbers.*

1) 1, 6, 2, 3

2) 12, 144, 1, 12

3) 16, 4, 8, 2

4) 9, 5, 27, 15

5) 7, 10, 60, 42

6) 8, 7, 24, 21

7) 10, 5, 8, 4

8) 3, 12, 8, 2

9) 2, 2, 1, 4

10) 3, 6, 7, 14

11) 2, 6, 5, 15

12) 7, 2, 14, 4

Similar Figures

Helpful	– Two or more figures are similar if the corresponding angles are equal, and the corresponding sides are in proportion.	**Example:**
Hints		3–4–5 triangle is similar to a 6–8–10 triangle

✍ **Each pair of figures is similar. Find the missing side.**

1)

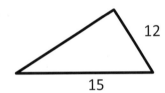 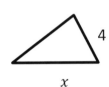

2)

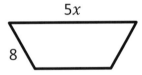 

3)

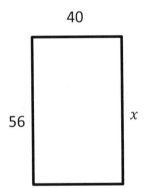 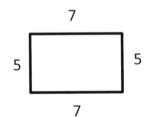

Simple Interest

Helpful	**Simple Interest:** The charge for borrowing money or the return for lending it.	**Example:**
Hints	Interest = principal x rate x time $$I = prt$$	$450 at 7% for 8 years. $$I = prt$$ $$I = 450 \times 0.07 \times 8 = \$252 =$$

✍ **Use simple interest to find the ending balance.**

1) $1,300 at 5% for 6 years.

2) $5,400 at 7.5% for 6 months.

3) $25,600 at 9.2% for 5 years

4) $24,000 at 8.5% for 9 years.

5) $450 at 7% for 8 years.

6) $54,200 at 8% for 5 years.

7) $240 interest is earned on a principal of $1500 at a simple interest rate of 4% interest per year. For how many years was the principal invested?

8) A new car, valued at $28,000, depreciates at 9% per year from original price. Find the value of the car 3 years after purchase.

9) Sara puts $2,000 into an investment yielding 5% annual simple interest; she left the money in for five years. How much interest does Sara get at the end of those five years?

Ratio and Rates Word Problems

Helpful *Hints*	To solve a ratio or a rate word problem, create a proportion and use cross multiplication method!	**Example:** $\dfrac{x}{4} = \dfrac{8}{16}$ $16x = 4 \times 8$ $x = 2$

✏ Solve.

1) In a party, 10 soft drinks are required for every 12 guests. If there are 252 guests, how many soft drink is required?

2) In Jack's class, 18 of the students are tall and 10 are short. In Michael's class 54 students are tall and 30 students are short. Which class has a higher ratio of tall to short students?

3) Are these ratios equivalent?

   12 cards to 72 animals 11 marbles to 66 marbles

4) The price of 3 apples at the Quick Market is $1.44. The price of 5 of the same apples at Walmart is $2.50. Which place is the better buy?

5) The bakers at a Bakery can make 160 bagels in 4 hours. How many bagels can they bake in 16 hours? What is that rate per hour?

6) You can buy 5 cans of green beans at a supermarket for $3.40. How much does it cost to buy 35 cans of green beans?

Answers of Worksheets – Chapter 3

Writing Ratios

1) $\frac{120\ miles}{4\ gallons}$, 30 miles per gallon

2) $\frac{24\ dollars}{6\ books}$, 4.00 dollars per book

3) $\frac{200\ miles}{14\ gallons}$, 14.29 miles per gallon

4) $\frac{24"\ of\ snow}{8\ hours}$, 3 inches of snow per hour

5) $\frac{1}{10}$

6) $\frac{3}{7}$

7) $\frac{2}{3}$

8) $\frac{1}{4}$

9) $\frac{1}{6}$

10) $\frac{9}{13}$

11) $\frac{1}{4}$

12) $\frac{2}{5}$

13) $\frac{8}{75}$

14) $\frac{12}{43}$

Simplifying Ratios

1) 3 : 7
2) 1 : 2
3) 1 : 5
4) 7 : 9
5) 5 : 3
6) 7 : 3
7) 10 : 1
8) 3 : 2

9) 7 : 9
10) 2 : 5
11) 5 : 7
12) 7 : 9
13) 26 : 41
14) 1 : 3
15) 8 : 1
16) 1 : 2

17) 1 : 12
18) 1 : 2
19) 3 : 50
20) 1 : 10
21) 1 : 6
22) 2 : 9
23) 17 : 20
24) 1 : 10

Create a Proportion

1) 1 : 3 = 2 : 6

2) 12 : 144 = 1 : 12

3) 2 : 4 = 8 : 16

4) 5 : 15 = 9 : 27

5) 7 : 42, 10 : 60

6) 7 : 21 = 8 : 24

7) 8 : 10 = 4 : 5

8) 2 : 3 = 8 : 12

9) 4 : 2 = 2 : 1

10) 7 : 3 = 14 : 6   11) 5 : 2 = 15 : 6   12) 7 : 2 = 14 : 4

Similar Figures

1) 5   2) 3   3) 56

Simple Interest

1) $1,690.00   4) $42,360.00   7) 4 years

2) $5,602.50   5) $702.00   8) $20,440

3) $37,376.00   6) $75,880.00   9) $500

Ratio and Rates Word Problems

1) 210

2) The ratio for both class is equal to 9 to 5.

3) Yes! Both ratios are 1 to 6

4) The price at the Quick Market is a better buy.

5) 640, the rate is 40 per hour.

6) $23.80

Chapter 4: Percent

Topics that you'll learn in this chapter:

✓ Percentage Calculations

✓ Converting Between Percent, Fractions, and Decimals

✓ Percent Problems

✓ Markup, Discount, and Tax

"Do not worry about your difficulties in mathematics. I can assure you mine are still greater." – Albert Einstein

Percentage Calculations

| *Helpful* | - | Use the following formula to find part, whole, or percent: | **Example:** |
| *Hints* | | $\text{part} = \dfrac{\text{percent}}{100} \times \text{whole}$ | $\dfrac{20}{100} \times 100 = 20$ |

✎ **Calculate the percentages.**

1) 50% of 25

2) 80% of 15

3) 30% of 34

4) 70% of 45

5) 10% of 0

6) 80% of 22

7) 65% of 8

8) 78% of 54

9) 50% of 80

10) 20% of 10

11) 40% of 40

12) 90% of 0

13) 20% of 70

14) 55% of 60

15) 80% of 10

16) 20% of 880

17) 70% of 100

18) 80% of 90

✎ **Solve.**

19) 50 is what percentage of 75?

20) What percentage of 100 is 70

21) Find what percentage of 60 is 35.

22) 40 is what percentage of 80?

Converting Between Percent, Fractions, and Decimals

Helpful *Hints*	– To a percent: Move the decimal point 2 places to the right and add the % symbol. **Examples:** – Divide by 100 to convert a number from percent to decimal. 30% = 0.3 0.24 = 24%

✎ **Converting fractions to decimals.**

1) $\dfrac{50}{100}$

2) $\dfrac{38}{100}$

3) $\dfrac{15}{100}$

4) $\dfrac{80}{100}$

5) $\dfrac{7}{100}$

6) $\dfrac{35}{100}$

7) $\dfrac{90}{100}$

8) $\dfrac{20}{100}$

9) $\dfrac{7}{100}$

✎ **Write each decimal as a percent.**

10) 0.5

11) 0.9

12) 0.002

13) 0.524

14) 0.1

15) 0.03

16) 3.63

17) 0.008

18) 4.78

Percent Problems

Helpful	Base = Part ÷ Percent	Example:
	Part = Percent × Base	2 is 10% of 20.
Hints	Percent = Part ÷ Base	2 ÷ 0.10 = 20
		2 = 0.10 × 20
		0.10 = 2 ÷ 20

✍ Solve each problem.

1) 51 is 340% of what?

2) 93% of what number is 97?

3) 27% of 142 is what number?

4) What percent of 125 is 29.3?

5) 60 is what percent of 126?

6) 67 is 67% of what?

7) 67 is 13% of what?

8) 41% of 78 is what?

9) 1 is what percent of 52.6?

10) What is 59% of 14 m?

11) What is 90% of 130 inches?

12) 16 inches is 35% of what?

13) 90% of 54.4 hours is what?

14) What percent of 33.5 is 21?

15) Liam scored 22 out of 30 marks in Algebra, 35 out of 40 marks in science and 89 out of 100 marks in mathematics. In which subject his percentage of marks in best?

16) Ella require 50% to pass. If she gets 280 marks and falls short by 20 marks, what were the maximum marks she could have got?

Markup, Discount, and Tax

Helpful	- **Markup** = selling price – cost	**Example:**

- **Markup** = selling price – cost
  Markup rate = markup divided by the cost

Helpful

Hints

- **Discount:**
  Multiply the regular price by the rate of discount

  Selling price =

  original price – discount

- **Tax:**
  To find tax, multiply the tax rate to the taxable amount (income, property value, etc.)

Example:

Original price of a microphone: $49.99, discount: 5%, tax: 5%

Selling price = 49.87

✎ *Find the selling price of each item.*

1) Cost of a pen: $1.95, markup: 70%, discount: 40%, tax: 5%

2) Cost of a puppy: $349.99, markup: 41%, discount: 23%

3) Cost of a shirt: $14.95, markup: 25%, discount: 45%

4) Cost of an oil change: $21.95, markup: 95%

5) Cost of computer: $1,850.00, markup: 75%

Answers of Worksheets – Chapter 4

Percentage Calculations

1) 12.5	9) 40	17) 70
2) 12	10) 2	18) 72
3) 10.2	11) 16	19) 67%
4) 31.5	12) 0	20) 70%
5) 0	13) 14	21) 58%
6) 17.6	14) 33	22) 50%
7) 5.2	15) 8	
8) 42.12	16) 176	

Converting Between Percent, Fractions, and Decimals

1) 0.5	7) 0.9	13) 52.4%
2) 0.38	8) 0.2	14) 10%
3) 0.15	9) 0.07	15) 3%
4) 0.8	10) 50%	16) 363%
5) 0.07	11) 90%	17) 0.8%
6) 0.35	12) 0.2%	18) 478%

Percent Problems

1) 15	7) 515.4	13) 49 hours
2) 104.3	8) 31.98	14) 62.7%
3) 38.34	9) 1.9%	15) Mathematics
4) 23.44%	10) 8.3 m	16) 600
5) 47.6%	11) 117 inches	
6) 100	12) 45.7 inches	

Markup, Discount, and Tax

1) $2.09

2) $379.98

3) $10.28

4) $36.22

5) $3,237.50

Chapter 5: Algebraic Expressions

Topics that you'll learn in this chapter:

- ✓ Expressions and Variables
- ✓ Simplifying Variable Expressions
- ✓ Simplifying Polynomial Expressions
- ✓ Translate Phrases into an Algebraic Statement
- ✓ The Distributive Property
- ✓ Evaluating One Variable
- ✓ Evaluating Two Variables
- ✓ Combining like Terms

Without mathematics, there's nothing you can do. Everything around you is mathematics. Everything around you is numbers." – Shakuntala Devi

Expressions and Variables

Helpful Hints

A variable is a letter that represents unknown numbers. A variable can be used in the same manner as all other numbers:

Addition	$2 + a$	2 plus a
Subtraction	$y - 3$	y minus 3
Division	$\dfrac{4}{x}$	4 divided by x
Multiplication	$5a$	5 times a

✍ **Simplify each expression.**

1) $x + 5x$,

   use $x = 5$

2) $8(-3x + 9) + 6$,

   use $x = 6$

3) $10x - 2x + 6 - 5$,

   use $x = 5$

4) $2x - 3x - 9$,

   use $x = 7$

5) $(-6)(-2x - 4y)$,

   use $x = 1$, $y = 3$

6) $8x + 2 + 4y$,

   use $x = 9$, $y = 2$

7) $(-6)(-8x - 9y)$,

   use $x = 5$, $y = 5$

8) $6x + 5y$,

   use $x = 7$, $y = 4$

✍ **Simplify each expression.**

9) $5(-4 + 2x)$

10) $-3 - 5x - 6x + 9$

11) $6x - 3x - 8 + 10$

12) $(-8)(6x - 4) + 12$

13) $9(7x + 4) + 6x$

14) $(-9)(-5x + 2)$

Simplifying Variable Expressions

Helpful	– Combine "like" terms. (values with same variable and same power)	**Example:**
Hints	– Use distributive property if necessary.	$2x + 2 (1 - 5x) =$
		$2x + 2 - 10x = -8x + 2$
	Distributive Property:	
	$a (b + c) = ab + ac$	

✍ Simplify each expression.

1) $-2 - x^2 - 6x^2$

2) $3 + 10x^2 + 2$

3) $8x^2 + 6x + 7x^2$

4) $5x^2 - 12x^2 + 8x$

5) $2x^2 - 2x - x$

6) $(-6)(8x - 4)$

7) $4x + 6 (2 - 5x)$

8) $10x + 8 (10x - 6)$

9) $9 (-2x - 6) - 5$

10) $3 (x + 9)$

11) $7x + 3 - 3x$

12) $2.5x^2 \times (-8x)$

✍ Simplify.

13) $-2(4 - 6x) - 3x, \ x = 1$

14) $2x + 8x, \ x = 2$

15) $9 - 2x + 5x + 2, \ x = 5$

16) $5 (3x + 7), \ x = 3$

17) $2 (3 - 2x) - 4, \ x = 6$

18) $5x + 3x - 8, \ x = 3$

19) $x - 7x, \ x = 8$

20) $5 (-2 - 9x), \ x = 4$

Simplifying Polynomial Expressions

Helpful		-	In mathematics, a polynomial is an expression consisting of variables and coefficients that involves only the operations of addition, subtraction, multiplication, and non–negative integer exponents of variables.	**Example:**

Helpful

Hints

In mathematics, a polynomial is an expression consisting of variables and coefficients that involves only the operations of addition, subtraction, multiplication, and non–negative integer exponents of variables.

$$P(x) = a_0x^n + a_1x^{n-1} + \ldots + a_{n-2}2x^2 + a_{n-1}x + a_n$$

Example:

An example of a polynomial of a single indeterminate x is

$x^2 - 4x + 7$.

An example for three variables is

$x^3 + 2xyz^2 - yz + 1$

✍ **Simplify each polynomial.**

1) $4x^5 - 5x^6 + 15x^5 - 12x^6 + 3 x^6$

2) $(- 3x^5 + 12 - 4x) + (8x^4 + 5x + 5 x^5)$

3) $10x^2 - 5x^4 + 14x^3 - 20x^4 + 15x^3 - 8x^4$

4) $- 6x^2 + 5x^2 - 7x^3 + 12 + 22$

5) $12x^5 - 5x^3 + 8x^2 - 8x^5$

6) $5x^3 + 1 + x^2 - 2x - 10x$

7) $14x^2 - 6x^3 - 2x (4x^2 + 2x)$

8) $(4x^4 - 2x) - (4x - 2x^4)$

9) $(3x^2 + 1) - (4 + 2x^2)$

10) $(2x + 2) - (7x + 6)$

11) $(12x^3 + 4x^4) - (2x^4 - 6x^3)$

12) $(12 + 3x^3) + (6x^3 + 6)$

13) $(5x^2 - 3) + (2x^2 - 3x^3)$

14) $(23x^3 - 12x^2) - (2x^2 - 9x^3)$

15) $(4x - 3x^3) - (3x^3 + 4x)$

Translate Phrases into an Algebraic Statement

Helpful	Translating key words and phrases into algebraic expressions:
	Addition: plus, more than, the sum of, etc.
Hints	**Subtraction:** minus, less than, decreased, etc.
	Multiplication: times, product, multiplied, etc.
	Division: quotient, divided, ratio, etc.
	Example:
	eight more than a number is 20
	$8 + x = 20$

✎ **Write an algebraic expression for each phrase.**

1) A number increased by forty–two. — $x + 42$

2) The sum of fifteen and a number — $15 + x$

3) The difference between fifty–six and a number. — $56 - n$

4) The quotient of thirty and a number. — $\dfrac{30}{n}$

5) Twice a number decreased by 25.

6) Four times the sum of a number and − 12.

7) A number divided by − 20.

8) The quotient of 60 and the product of a number and − 5.

9) Ten subtracted from a number.

10) The difference of six and a number.

The Distributive Property

> *Helpful*
>
> *Hints*
>
> Distributive Property:
>
> $a\,(b\,+\,c)\,=\,ab\,+\,ac$
>
> **Example:**
>
> $3\,(4\,+\,3x)$
>
> $=\,12\,+\,9x$

✎**Use the distributive property to simply each expression.**

1) $-(-2-5x)$

2) $(-6x+2)(-1)$

3) $(-5)\,(x-2)$

4) $-(7-3x)$

5) $8\,(8+2x)$

6) $2\,(12+2x)$

7) $(-6x+8)\,4$

8) $(3-6x)(-7)$

9) $(-12)\,(2x+1)$

10) $(8-2x)\,9$

11) $(-2x)\,(-1+9x)-4x\,(4+5x)$

12) $3\,(-5x-3)+4(6-3x)$

13) $(-2)(x+4)-(2+3x)$

14) $(-4)(3x-2)+6\,(x+1)$

15) $(-5)(4x-1)+4\,(x+2)$

16) $(-3)(x+4)-(2+3x)$

Evaluating One Variable

Helpful	– To evaluate one variable expression, find the variable and substitute a number for that variable.	**Example:**
Hints	– Perform the arithmetic operations.	$4x + 8, x = 6$ $4(6) + 8 = 24 + 8 = 32$

✍ *Simplify each algebraic expression.*

1) $9 - x$, $x = 3$

2) $x + 2$, $x = 5$

3) $3x + 7$, $x = 6$

4) $x + (-5)$, $x = -2$

5) $3x + 6$, $x = 4$

6) $4x + 6$, $x = -1$

7) $10 + 2x - 6$, $x = 3$

8) $10 - 3x$, $x = 8$

15) $8(5x - 12)$, $x = -2$

9) $\dfrac{20}{x} - 3$, $x = 5$

10) $(-3) + \dfrac{x}{4} + 2x$, $x = 16$

11) $(-2) + \dfrac{x}{7}$, $x = 21$

12) $(-\dfrac{14}{x}) - 9 + 4x$, $x = 2$

13) $(-\dfrac{6}{x}) - 9 + 2x$, $x = 3$

14) $(-2) + \dfrac{x}{8}$, $x = 16$

Evaluating Two Variables

Helpful	To evaluate an algebraic expression, substitute a number for each variable and perform the arithmetic operations.	**Example:**
Hints		$2x + 4y - 3 + 2,$ $x = 5, y = 3$ $2(5) + 4(3) - 3 + 2$ $= 10$ $+ 12 - 3 + 2$ $= 21$

✍ Simplify each algebraic expression.

1) $2x + 4y - 3 + 2,$

   $x = 5, y = 3$

2) $(-\dfrac{12}{x}) + 1 + 5y,$

   $x = 6, y = 8$

3) $(-4)(-2a - 2b),$

   $a = 5, b = 3$

4) $10 + 3x + 7 - 2y,$

   $x = 7, y = 6$

5) $9x + 2 - 4y,$

   $x = 7, y = 5$

6) $6 + 3(-2x - 3y),$

   $x = 9, y = 7$

7) $12x + y,$

   $x = 4, y = 8$

8) $x \times 4 \div y,$

   $x = 3, y = 2$

9) $2x + 14 + 4y,$

   $x = 6, y = 8$

10) $4a - (5 - b),$

   $a = 4, b = 6$

Combining like Terms

Helpful *Hints*	– Terms are separated by "+" and "–" signs. – Like terms are terms with same variables and same powers. – Be sure to use the "+" or "–" that is in front of the coefficient.	**Example:** $22x + 6 + 2x =$ $24x + 6$

✎ **Simplify each expression.**

1) $5 + 2x - 8$

2) $(-2x + 6)\,2$

3) $7 + 3x + 6x - 4$

4) $(-4) - (3)(5x + 8)$

5) $9x - 7x - 5$

6) $x - 12x$

7) $7\,(3x + 6) + 2x$

8) $(-11x) - 10x$

9) $3x - 12 - 5x$

10) $13 + 4x - 5$

11) $(-22x) + 8x$

12) $2\,(4 + 3x) - 7x$

13) $(-4x) - (6 - 14x)$

14) $5\,(6x - 1) + 12x$

15) $22x + 6 + 2x$

16) $(-13x) - 14x$

17) $(-6x) - 9 + 15x$

18) $(-6x) + 7x$

19) $(-5x) + 12 + 7x$

20) $(-3x) - 9 + 15x$

21) $20x - 19x$

Answers of Worksheets – Chapter 5

Expressions and Variables

1) 30
2) −66
3) 41
4) −16
5) 84

6) 82
7) 510
8) 62
9) $10x - 20$
10) $6 - 11x$

11) $3x + 2$
12) $44 - 48x$
13) $69x + 36$
14) $45x - 18$

Simplifying Variable Expressions

1) $-7x^2 - 2$
2) $10x^2 + 5$
3) $15x^2 + 6x$
4) $-7x^2 + 8x$
5) $2x^2 - 3x$
6) $-48x + 24$
7) $-26x + 12$

8) $90x - 48$
9) $-18x - 59$
10) $3x + 27$
11) $4x + 3$
12) $-20x^3$
13) 1
14) 20

15) 26
16) 80
17) -22
18) 16
19) -48
20) -190

Simplifying Polynomial Expressions

1) $-14x^6 + 19x^5$
2) $2x^5 + 8x^4 + x + 12$
3) $-33x^4 + 29x^3 + 10x^2$
4) $-7x^3 - x^2 + 34$
5) $4x^5 - 5x^3 + 8x^2$
6) $5x^3 + x^2 - 12x + 1$
7) $-14x^3 + 10x^2$
8) $6x^4 - 6x$

9) $x^2 - 3$
10) $-5x - 4$
11) $2x^4 + 18x^3$
12) $9x^3 + 18$
13) $-3x^3 + 7x^2 - 3$
14) $32x^3 - 14x^2$
15) $-6x^3$

Translate Phrases into an Algebraic Statement

1) $x + 42$
3) $56 - x$
4) $30/x$
5) $2x - 25$
8) $\dfrac{60}{-5x}$

2) $15 + x$
6) $4(x + (-12))$
7) $\dfrac{x}{-20}$
9) $x - 10$
10) $6 - x$

The Distributive Property

1) $5x + 2$
2) $6x - 2$
3) $-5x + 10$
4) $3x - 7$
5) $16x + 64$
6) $4x + 24$

7) $-24x + 32$
8) $42x - 21$
9) $-24x - 12$
10) $-18x + 72$
11) $-38x^2 - 14x$
12) $-27x + 15$

13) $-5x - 10$
14) $-6x + 14$
15) $-16x + 13$
16) $-6x - 14$

Evaluating One Variable

1) 6
2) 7
3) 25
4) -7
5) 18

6) 2
7) 10
8) -14
9) 1
10) 33

11) 1
12) -8
13) -5
14) 0
15) -176

Evaluating Two Variables

1) 21
2) 39
3) 64
4) 26

5) 45
6) -111
7) 56
8) 6

9) 58
10) 17

Combining like Terms

1) $2x - 3$
2) $-4x + 12$
3) $9x + 3$
4) $-15x - 28$
5) $2x - 5$
6) $-11x$
7) $23x + 42$

8) $-21x$
9) $-2x - 12$
10) $4x + 8$
11) $-14x$
12) $-x + 8$
13) $10x - 6$
14) $42x - 5$

15) $24x + 6$
16) $-27x$
17) $9x - 9$
18) x
19) $2x + 12$
20) $12x - 9$
21) x

Chapter 6: Equations

Topics that you'll learn in this chapter:

- ✓ One– Step Equations
- ✓ Two– Step Equations
- ✓ Multi– Step Equations

"The study of mathematics, like the Nile, begins in minuteness but ends in magnificence."

– Charles Caleb Colton

One–Step Equations

| *Helpful* *Hints* | - The values of two expressions on both sides of an equation are equal. $$ax + b = c$$ - You only need to perform one Math operation in order to solve the equation. | **Example:** $$-8x = 16$$ $$x = -2$$ |

✎ **Solve each equation.**

1) $x + 3 = 17$

2) $22 = (-8) + x$

3) $3x = (-30)$

4) $(-36) = (-6x)$

5) $(-6) = 4 + x$

6) $2 + x = (-2)$

7) $20x = (-220)$

8) $18 = x + 5$

9) $(-23) + x = (-19)$

10) $5x = (-45)$

11) $x - 12 = (-25)$

12) $x - 3 = (-12)$

13) $(-35) = x - 27$

14) $8 = 2x$

15) $(-6x) = 36$

16) $(-55) = (-5x)$

17) $x - 30 = 20$

18) $8x = 32$

19) $36 = (-4x)$

20) $4x = 68$

21) $30x = 300$

Two–Step Equations

Helpful	– You only need to perform two math operations (add, subtract, multiply, or divide) to solve the equation.	Example:
Hints	– Simplify using the inverse of addition or subtraction.	$-2(x-1) = 42$ $(x-1) = -21$
	– Simplify further by using the inverse of multiplication or division.	$x = -20$

✍ Solve each equation.

1) $5(8 + x) = 20$

2) $(-7)(x - 9) = 42$

3) $(-12)(2x - 3) = (-12)$

4) $6(1 + x) = 12$

5) $12(2x + 4) = 60$

6) $7(3x + 2) = 42$

7) $8(14 + 2x) = (-34)$

8) $(-15)(2x - 4) = 48$

9) $3(x + 5) = 12$

10) $\dfrac{3x - 12}{6} = 4$

11) $(-12) = \dfrac{x + 15}{6}$

12) $110 = (-5)(2x - 6)$

13) $\dfrac{x}{8} - 12 = 4$

14) $20 = 12 + \dfrac{x}{4}$

15) $\dfrac{-24 + x}{6} = (-12)$

16) $(-4)(5 + 2x) = (-100)$

17) $(-12x) + 20 = 32$

18) $\dfrac{-2 + 6x}{4} = (-8)$

19) $\dfrac{x + 6}{5} = (-5)$

20) $(-9) + \dfrac{x}{4} = (-15)$

Multi–Step Equations

Helpful *Hints*	– Combine "like" terms on one side. – Bring variables to one side by adding or subtracting. – Simplify using the inverse of addition or subtraction. – Simplify further by using the inverse of multiplication or division.	**Example:** $3x + 15 = -2x + 5$ Add 2x both sides $5x + 15 = +5$ Subtract 15 both sides $5x = -10$ Divide by 5 both sides $x = -2$

✎ *Solve each equation.*

1) $-(2 - 2x) = 10$

2) $-12 = -(2x + 8)$

3) $3x + 15 = (-2x) + 5$

4) $-28 = (-2x) - 12x$

5) $2(1 + 2x) + 2x = -118$

6) $3x - 18 = 22 + x - 3 + x$

7) $12 - 2x = (-32) - x + x$

8) $7 - 3x - 3x = 3 - 3x$

9) $6 + 10x + 3x = (-30) + 4x$

10) $(-3x) - 8(-1 + 5x) = 352$

11) $24 = (-4x) - 8 + 8$

12) $9 = 2x - 7 + 6x$

13) $6(1 + 6x) = 294$

14) $-10 = (-4x) - 6x$

15) $4x - 2 = (-7) + 5x$

16) $5x - 14 = 8x + 4$

17) $40 = -(4x - 8)$

18) $(-18) - 6x = 6(1 + 3x)$

19) $x - 5 = -2(6 + 3x)$

20) $6 = 1 - 2x + 5$

Answers of Worksheets – Chapter 6

One–Step Equations

1) 14
2) 30
3) − 10
4) 6
5) − 10
6) − 4
7) − 11

8) 13
9) 4
10) − 9
11) − 13
12) − 9
13) − 8
14) 4

15) − 6
16) 11
17) 50
18) 4
19) − 9
20) 17
21) 10

Two–Step Equations

1) − 4
2) 3
3) 2
4) 1
5) 0.5
6) $\frac{4}{3}$
7) $-\frac{73}{8}$

8) $\frac{2}{5}$
9) − 1
10) 12
11) − 87
12) − 8
13) 128
14) 32

15) − 48
16) 10
17) − 1
18) − 5
19) − 31
20) − 24

Multi–Step Equations

1) 6
2) 2
3) − 2
4) 2
5) − 20
6) 37
7) 22

8) $\frac{4}{3}$
9) − 4
10) − 8
11) − 6
12) 2
13) 8

14) 1
15) 5
16) − 6
17) − 8
18) − 1
19) − 1
20) 0

Chapter 7: Inequalities

Topics that you'll learn in this chapter:

- ✓ Graphing Single– Variable Inequalities
- ✓ One– Step Inequalities
- ✓ Two– Step Inequalities
- ✓ Multi– Step Inequalities

Without mathematics, there's nothing you can do. Everything around you is mathematics. Everything around you is numbers." – Shakuntala Devi

Graphing Single–Variable Inequalities

Helpful	– Isolate the variable.
	– Find the value of the inequality on the number line.
Hints	– For less than or greater than draw open circle on the value of the variable.
	– If there is an equal sign too, then use filled circle.
	– Draw a line to the right direction.

✎ **Draw a graph for each inequality.**

1) $-2 > x$

-10 -9 -8 -7 -6 -5 -4 -3 -2 -1 0 1 2 3 4 5 6 7 8 9 10

2) $5 \leq -x$

-10 -9 -8 -7 -6 -5 -4 -3 -2 -1 0 1 2 3 4 5 6 7 8 9 10

3) $x > 7$

-10 -9 -8 -7 -6 -5 -4 -3 -2 -1 0 1 2 3 4 5 6 7 8 9 10

4) $-x > 1.5$

-10 -9 -8 -7 -6 -5 -4 -3 -2 -1 0 1 2 3 4 5 6 7 8 9 10

One–Step Inequalities

Helpful *Hints*	– Isolate the variable. – For dividing both sides by negative numbers, flip the direction of the inequality sign.	**Example:** $x + 4 \geq 11$ $x \geq 7$

✎ **Solve each inequality and graph it.**

1) $x + 9 \geq 11$
$9 \geq 9$
$x = \dfrac{2}{2}$

2) $x - 4 \leq 2$
$4 \quad 4$

3) $6x \geq 36$

4) $7 + x < 16$

5) $x + 8 \leq 1$

6) $3x > 12$

7) $3x < 24$

Two–Step Inequalities

Helpful *Hints*	– Isolate the variable. – For dividing both sides by negative numbers, flip the direction of the of the inequality sign. – Simplify using the inverse of addition or subtraction. – Simplify further by using the inverse of multiplication or division.	**Example:** $2x + 9 \geq 11$ $2x \geq 2$ $x \geq 1$

✎ **Solve each inequality and graph it.**

1) $3x - 4 \leq 5$

2) $2x - 2 \leq 6$

3) $4x - 4 \leq 8$

4) $3x + 6 \geq 12$

5) $6x - 5 \geq 19$

6) $2x - 4 \leq 6$

7) $8x - 4 \leq 4$

8) $6x + 4 \leq 10$

9) $5x + 4 \leq 9$

10) $7x - 4 \leq 3$

11) $4x - 19 < 19$

12) $2x - 3 < 21$

13) $7 + 4x \geq 19$

14) $9 + 4x < 21$

15) $3 + 2x \geq 19$

16) $6 + 4x < 22$

Multi–Step Inequalities

Helpful *Hints*	– Isolate the variable. – Simplify using the inverse of addition or subtraction. – Simplify further by using the inverse of multiplication or division.	**Example:** $\dfrac{7x+1}{3} \geq 5$ $7x + 1 \geq 15$ $7x \geq 14$ $x \geq 7$

✍ *Solve each inequality.*

1) $\dfrac{9x}{7} - 7 < 2$

2) $\dfrac{4x+8}{2} \leq 12$

3) $\dfrac{3x-8}{7} > 1$

4) $-3\,(x-7) > 21$

5) $4 + \dfrac{x}{3} < 7$

6) $\dfrac{2x+6}{4} \leq 10$

Answers of Worksheets – Chapter 7

Graphing Single–Variable Inequalities

1) $-2 > x$

2) $x \leq - 5$

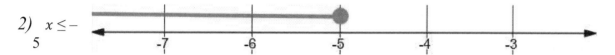

3) $x > 7$

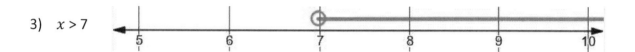

4) $-1.5 > x$

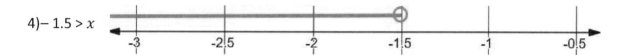

One–Step Inequalities

1)

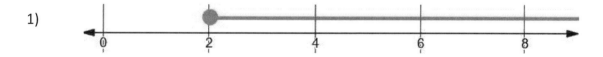

2)

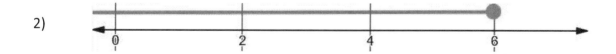

3)

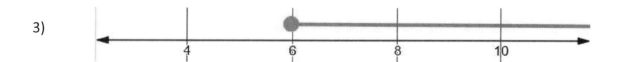

4)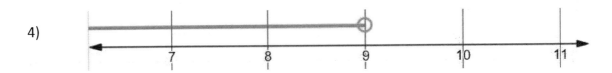

5)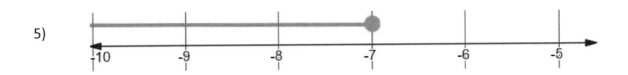

6)

7)

Two–Step inequalities

1) $x \leq 3$

2) $x \leq 4$

3) $x \leq 3$

4) $x \geq 2$

5) $x \geq 4$

6) $x \leq 5$

7) $x \leq 1$

8) $x \leq 1$

9) $x \leq 1$

10) $x \leq 1$

11) $x < 9.5$

12) $x < 12$

13) $x \geq 3$

14) $x < 3$

15) $x \geq 8$

16) $x < 4$

Multi–Step inequalities

1) $x < 7$

2) $x \leq 4$

3) $x > 5$

4) $x < 0$

5) $x < 9$

6) $x \leq 17$

Chapter 8: Linear Functions

Topics that you'll learn in this chapter:

- ✓ Finding Slope
- ✓ Graphing Lines Using Slope– Intercept Form
- ✓ Graphing Lines Using Standard Form
- ✓ Writing Linear Equations
- ✓ Graphing Linear Inequalities
- ✓ Finding Midpoint
- ✓ Finding Distance of Two Points

"Sometimes the questions are complicated and the answers are simple." – Dr. Seuss

Finding Slope

Helpful	Slope of a line:	Example:
Hins	$$\dfrac{y_2 - y_1}{x_2 - x_1} = \dfrac{rise}{run}$$	$(2, -10), (3, 6)$ slope = 16

🖋 **Find the slope of the line through each pair of points.**

1) $(1, 1), (3, 5)$

2) $(4, -6), (-3, -8)$

3) $(7, -12), (5, 10)$

4) $(19, 3), (20, 3)$

5) $(15, 8), (-17, 9)$

6) $(6, -12), (15, -3)$

7) $(3, 1), (7, -5)$

8) $(3, -2), (-7, 8)$

9) $(15, -3), (-9, 5)$

10) $(-4, 7), (-6, -4)$

11) $(6, -8), (-11, -7)$

12) $(-6, 13), (17, -9)$

13) $(-10, -2), (-6, -5)$

14) $(4, 5), (-4, 10)$

15) $(-3, 1), (-17, 2)$

16) $(7, 0), (-13, -11)$

17) $(17, -13), (17, 8)$

18) $(12, 2), (-7, 5)$

Graphing Lines Using Slope–Intercept Form

Helpful	**Slope–intercept form:** given the slope m and the y–intercept b, then the equation of the line is:
Hints	$y = mx + b$.

Example:

$y = 8x - 3$

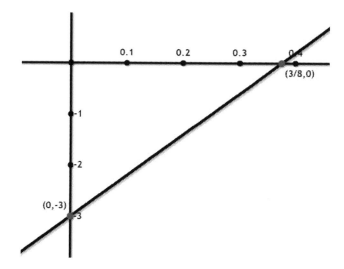

🖎 **Sketch the graph of each line.**

1) $y = \dfrac{1}{2} x - 4$

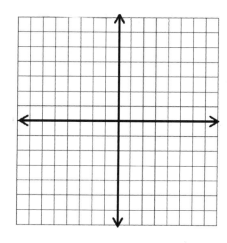

2) $y = 2x$

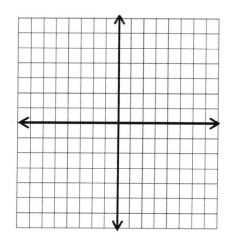

Graphing Lines Using Standard Form

Helpful	— Find the –intercept of the line by putting zero for y.
Hints	— Find the y–intercept of the line by putting zero for the x.
	— Connect these two points.

Example:

$x + 4y = 12$

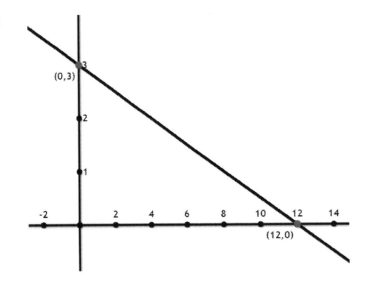

✎ **Sketch the graph of each line.**

1) $2x - y = 4$

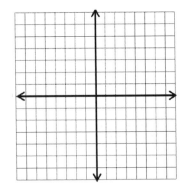

2) $x + y = 2$

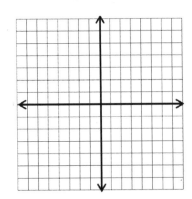

Writing Linear Equations

Helpful *Hints*	The equation of a line: $$y = mx + b$$ 1– Identify the slope. 2– Find the y–intercept. This can be done by substituting the slope and the coordinates of a point (x, y) on the line.	**Example:** through: $(-4, -2), (-3, 5)$ $y = 7x + 26$

✍ *Write the slope–intercept form of the equation of the line through the given points.*

1) through: $(-4, -2), (-3, 5)$

2) through: $(5, 4), (-4, 3)$

3) through: $(0, -2), (-5, 3)$

4) through: $(-1, 1), (-2, 6)$

5) through: $(0, 3), (-4, -1)$

6) through: $(0, 2), (1, -3)$

7) through: $(0, -5), (4, 3)$

8) through: $(-1, 4), (0, 4)$

9) through: $(2, -3), (3, -5)$

10) through: $(2, 5), (-1, -4)$

11) through: $(1, -3), (-3, 1)$

12) through: $(3, 3), (1, -5)$

13) through: $(4, 4), (3, -5)$

14) through: $(0, 3), (1, 1)$

15) through: $(5, 5), (2, -3)$

16) through: $(-2, -2), (2, -5)$

17) through: $(-3, -2), (1, -1)$

18) through: $(-2, 1), (6, 5)$

Graphing Linear Inequalities

Helpful	1– First, graph the "equals" line.
	2– Choose a testing point. (it can be any point on both sides of the line.)
Hints	3– Put the value of (x, y) of that point in the inequality. If that works, that part of the line is the solution. If the values don't work, then the other part of the line is the solution.

✏️ *Sketch the graph of each linear inequality.*

1) $y < -4x + 2$

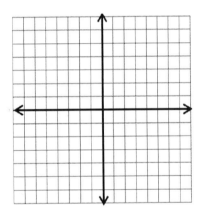

2) $2x + y < -4$

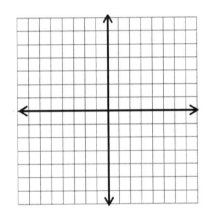

4) $x - 3y < -5$

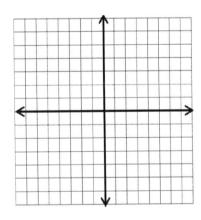

5) $6x - 2y \geq 8$

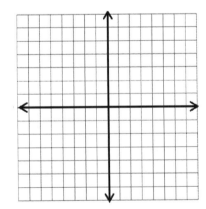

Finding Midpoint

Helpful *Hints*	Midpoint of the segment AB: $\qquad$ **Example:**

$$M\left(\frac{x_1+x_2}{2}, \frac{y_1+y_2}{2}\right)$$

(3, 9), (− 1, 6)

M (1, 7.5)

✎ **Find the midpoint of the line segment with the given endpoints.**

1) (2, − 2), (3, − 5)

2) (0, 2), (− 2, − 6)

3) (7, 4), (9, − 1)

4) (4, − 5), (0, 8)

5) (1, − 2), (1, − 6)

6) (− 2, − 3), (3, − 6)

7) (7, 0), (− 7, 5)

8) (− 2, 6), (− 3, − 2)

9) (− 1, 1), (5, − 5)

10) (2.3, − 1.3), (− 2.2, − 0.5)

11) (4.1, 6.32), (4, 5.6)

12) (2, − 1), (− 6, 0)

13) (− 4, 4), (5, − 1)

14) (− 2, − 3), (− 6, 5)

15) ($\frac{1}{2}$, 1), (2, 4)

16) (− 2, − 2), (6, 5)

Finding Distance of Two Points

Helpful *Hints*	Distance from A to B: $$d = \sqrt{(x_1 - x_2)^2 + (y_1 - y_2)^2}$$	**Example:** $(-1, 2), (-1, -7)$ Distance = 9

✎ *Find the distance between each pair of points.*

1) $(2, -1), (1, -1)$

2) $(6, 4), (-1, 3)$

3) $(-8, -5), (-6, 1)$

4) $(-6, -10), (-2, -10)$

5) $(4, -6), (-3, 4)$

6) $(-6, -7), (-2, -8)$

7) $(5, 4), (8, 2)$

8) $(8, 4), (3, -7)$

9) $(1, 3), (5, 7)$

10) $(4, 2), (-7, 1)$

11) $(-3, -4), (-7, -2)$

12) $(-7, -2), (6, 9)$

13) $(10, 0), (0, 4)$

14) $(-3, 2), (5, 0)$

15) $(-5, 6), (8, -4)$

16) $(3, -5), (-8, -4)$

17) $(0, 8), (4, 10)$

18) $(6, 4), (-5, -1)$

Answers of Worksheets – Chapter 8

Finding Slope

1) 2

2) $\dfrac{2}{7}$

3) −11

4) 0

5) $-\dfrac{1}{32}$

6) 1

7) $-\dfrac{3}{2}$

8) −1

9) $-\dfrac{1}{3}$

10) $\dfrac{11}{2}$

11) $-\dfrac{1}{17}$

12) $-\dfrac{22}{23}$

13) $-\dfrac{3}{4}$

14) $-\dfrac{5}{8}$

15) $-\dfrac{1}{14}$

16) $\dfrac{11}{20}$

17) Undefined

18) $-\dfrac{3}{19}$

Graphing Lines Using Slope–Intercept Form

1)

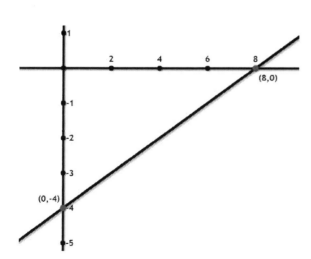

2)

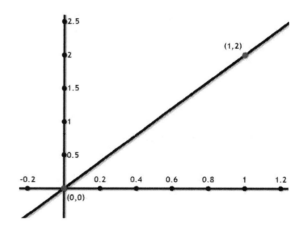

Graphing Lines Using Standard Form

1)

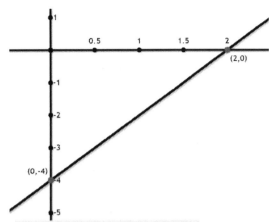

2)

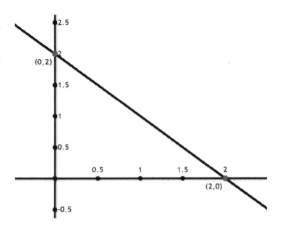

Writing Linear Equations

1) $y = 7x + 26$

2) $y = \frac{1}{9}x + \frac{31}{9}$

3) $y = -x - 2$

4) $y = -5x - 4$

5) $y = x + 3$

6) $y = -5x + 2$

7) $y = 2x - 5$

8) $y = 4$

9) $y = -2x + 1$

10) $y = 3x - 1$

11) $y = -x - 2$

12) $y = 4x - 9$

13) $y = 9x - 32$

14) $y = -2x + 3$

15) $y = \frac{8}{3}x - \frac{25}{3}$

16) $y = -\frac{3}{4}x - \frac{7}{2}$

17) $y = \frac{1}{4}x - \frac{5}{4}$

18) $y = -\frac{4}{3}x + \frac{19}{3}$

Graphing Linear Inequalities

1)

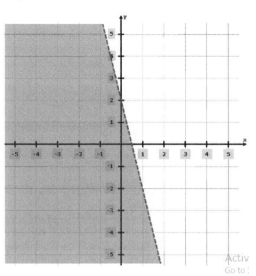

2)

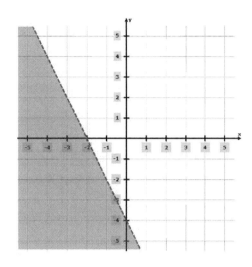

4)

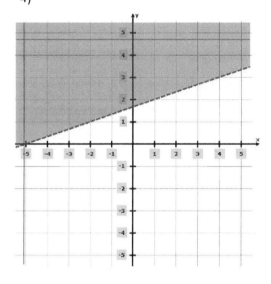

5)

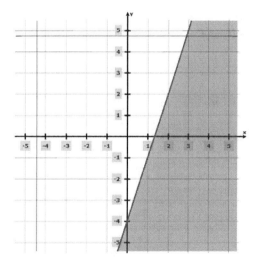

Finding Midpoint

1) (2.5, −3.5)

2) (−1, −2)

3) (8, 1.5)

4) (2, 1.5)

5) (1, −4)

6) (0.5, −4.5)

7) (0, 2.5)

8) (−2.5, 2)

9) (2, −2)

10) (0.05, −0.9)

11) (4.05, 5.96)

12) (−2, − 0.5)

13) $(\frac{1}{2}, 1\frac{1}{2})$

14) (−4, 1)

15) (1.25, 2.5)

16) $(2, \frac{3}{2})$

Finding Distance of Two Points

1) 1

2) 7.1

3) 6.32

4) 4

5) 12.21

6) 4.12

7) 3.61

8) 12.1

9) 5.66

10) 11.04

11) 4.47

12) 17.03

13) 10.77

14) 8.25

15) 16.4

16) 10.3

17) 4.47

18) 12.1

Chapter 9: Polynomials

Topics that you'll learn in this chapter:

- ✓ Classifying Polynomials
- ✓ Writing Polynomials in Standard Form
- ✓ Simplifying Polynomials
- ✓ Adding and Subtracting Polynomials
- ✓ Multiplying Monomials
- ✓ Multiplying and Dividing Monomials
- ✓ Multiplying a Polynomial and a Monomial
- ✓ Multiplying Binomials
- ✓ Factoring Trinomials
- ✓ Operations with Polynomials

Mathematics – the unshaken Foundation of Sciences, and the plentiful Fountain of Advantage to human affairs. —

Isaac Barrow

Classifying Polynomials

Helpful	Name	Degree	Example
	constant	0	4
Hints	linear	1	$2x$
	quadratic	2	$x^2 + 5x + 6$
	cubic	3	$x^3 - x^2 + 4x + 8$
	quartic	4	$x^4 + 3x^3 - x^2 + 2x + 6$
	quantic	5	$x^5 - 2x^4 + x^3 - x^2 + x + 10$

✎ *Name each polynomial by degree and number of terms.*

1) x monomail linear

2) $-5x^4$ quartic monomial

3) $7x - 4$ linear binomial
   constant monomial

4) -6

5) $8x + 1$ linear binomial

6) $9x^2 - 8x^3$ cubic binomial

7) $2x^5$ quartic monomial

8) $10 + 8x$ linear binomial

9) $5x^2 - 6x$ quadrate binomial

10) $-7x^7 + 7x^4$ degree binomial

11) $-8x^4 + 5x^3 - 2x^2 - 8x$ quartic poly

12) $4x - 9x^2 + 4x^3 - 5x^4$ quatic poly

13) $4x^6 + 5x^5 + x^4$ degree cubic

14) $-4 - 2x^2 + 8x$ quadratic bi

15) $9x^6 - 8$ linear binomial

16) $7x^5 + 10x^4 - 3x + 10x^7$ degree qu

17) $4x^6 - 3x^2 - 8x^4$ degree cubic

18) $-5x^4 + 10x - 10$ quantic cubi

Writing Polynomials in Standard Form

Helpful	A polynomial function $f(x)$ of degree n is of the form	**Example:**
Hints	$f(x) = a_n x^n + a_{n-1} x^{n-1} + \ldots + a_1 x + a_0$	$2x^2 - 4x^3 - x =$
	The first term is the one with the biggest power!	$-4x^3 + 2x^2 - x$

✍ *Write each polynomial in standard form.*

1) $3x^2 - 5x^3$

2) $3 + 4x^3 - 3$

3) $2x^2 + 1x - 6x^3$

4) $9x - 7x$

5) $12 - 7x + 9x^4$

6) $5x^2 + 13x - 2x^3$

7) $-3 + 16x - 16x$

8) $3x(x + 4) - 2(x + 4)$

9) $(x + 5)(x - 2)$

10) $3x^2 + x + 12 - 5x^2 - 2x$

11) $12x^5 + 7x^3 - 3x^5 - 8x^3$

12) $3x(2x + 5 - 2x^2)$

13) $11x(x^5 + 2x^3)$

14) $(x + 6)(x + 3)$

15) $(x + 4)^2$

16) $(8x - 7)(3x + 2)$

17) $5x(3x^2 + 2x + 1)$

18) $7x(3 - x + 6x^3)$

Simplifying Polynomials

Helpful	1– Find "like" terms. (they have same variables with same power).	Example:
Hints	2– Add or Subtract "like" terms using PEMDAS operation.	$2x^5 - 3x^3 + 8x^2 - 2x^5 =$ $-3x^3 + 8x^2$

✍ *Simplify each expression.*

1) $11 - 4x^2 + 3x^2 - 7x^3 + 3$

2) $2x^5 - x^3 + 8x^2 - 2x^5$

3) $(-5)(x^6 + 10) - 8(14 - x^6)$

4) $4(2x^2 + 4x^2 - 3x^3) + 6x^3 + 17$

5) $11 - 6x^2 + 5x^2 - 12x^3 + 22$

6) $2x^2 - 2x + 3x^3 + 12x - 22x$

7) $(3x - 8)(3x - 4)$

8) $(12x + 2y)^2$

9) $(12x^3 + 28x^2 + 10x + 4) \div (x + 2)$

10) $(2x + 12x^2 - 2) \div (2x + 1)$

11) $(2x^3 - 1) + (3x^3 - 2x^3)$

12) $(x - 5)(x - 3)$

13) $(3x + 8)(3x - 8)$

14) $(8x^2 - 3x) - (5x - 5 - 8x^2)$

Adding and Subtracting Polynomials

Helpful	Adding polynomials is just a matter of combining like terms, with some order of operations considerations thrown in.	**Example:**
Hints	Be careful with the minus signs, and don't confuse addition and multiplication!	$(3x^3 - 1) - (4x^3 + 2)$ $= -x^3 - 3$

✍ **Simplify each expression.**

1) $(2x^3 - 2) + (2x^3 + 2)$

2) $(4x^3 + 5) - (7 - 2x^3)$

3) $(4x^2 + 2x^3) - (2x^3 + 5)$

4) $(4x^2 - x) + (3x - 5x^2)$

5) $(7x + 9) - (3x + 9)$

6) $(4x^4 - 2x) - (6x - 2x^4)$

7) $(12x - 4x^3) - (8x^3 + 6x)$

8) $(2x^3 - 8x^2) - (5x^2 - 3x^3)$

9) $(2x^2 - 6) + (9x^2 - 4x^3)$

10) $(4x^3 + 3x^4) - (x^4 - 5x^3)$

11) $(-12x^4 + 10x^5 + 2x^3) + (14x^3 + 23x^5 + 8x^4)$

12) $(13x^2 - 6x^5 - 2x) - (-10x^2 - 11x^5 + 9x)$

13) $(35 + 9x^5 - 3x^2) + (8x^4 + 3x^5) - (27 - 5x^4)$

14) $(3x^5 - 2x^3 - 4x) + (4x + 10x^4 - 23) + (x^2 - x^3 + 12)$

Multiplying Monomials

Helpful	A monomial is a polynomial with just one term,	**Example:**
Hints	like $2x$ or $7y$.	$2u^3 \times (-3u)$
		$= -6u^4$

✎ *Simplify each expression.*

1) $2xy^2z \times 4z^2$

2) $4xy \times x^2y$

3) $4pq^3 \times (-2p^4q)$

4) $8s^4t^2 \times st^5$

5) $12p^3 \times (-3p^4)$

6) $-4p^2q^3r \times 6pq^2r^3$

7) $(-8a^4) \times (-12a^6b)$

8) $3u^4v^2 \times (-7u^2v^3)$

9) $4u^3 \times (-2u)$

10) $-6xy^2 \times 3x^2y$

11) $12y^2z^3 \times (-y^2z)$

12) $5a^2bc^2 \times 2abc^2$

Multiplying and Dividing Monomials

Helpful	- When you divide two monomials you need to divide their coefficients and then divide their variables.
Hints	- In case of exponents with the same base, you need to subtract their powers.

Example:

$$(-3x^2)(8x^4y^{12}) = -24x^6y^{12}$$

$$\frac{36\,x^5y^7}{4\,x^4y^5} = 9xy^2$$

✎ **Simplify.**

1) $(7x^4y^6)(4x^3y^4)$

2) $(15x^4)\,(3x^9)$

3) $(12x^2y^9)(7x^9y^{12})$

4) $\dfrac{80x^{12}y^9}{10x^6y^7}$

5) $\dfrac{95x^{18}y^7}{5x^9y^2}$

6) $\dfrac{200x^3y^8}{40x^3y^7}$

7) $\dfrac{-15x^{17}y^{13}}{3x^6y^9}$

8) $\dfrac{-64x^8y^{10}}{8x^3y^7}$

Multiplying a Polynomial and a Monomial

Helpful	– When multiplying monomials, use the product rule for exponents.	**Example:**
Hints	– When multiplying a monomial by a polynomial, use the distributive property.	$2x(8x-2) =$
	$a \times (b+c) = a \times b + a \times c$	$16x^2 - 4x$

✍️ **Find each product.**

1) $5(3x - 6y)$

$15x = 30y$

2) $9x(2x + 4y)$

$18x^2 + 36xy$

3) $8x(7x - 4)$

$56x^2 - 32x$

4) $12x(3x + 9)$

$36x^2 + 108x$

5) $11x(2x - 11y)$

$22x^2 - 121xy$

6) $2x(6x - 6y)$

$12x^2 - 12xy$

7) $3x(2x^2 - 3x + 8)$

$6x^3 - 9x^2 + 24$

8) $13x(4x + 8y)$

$52x^2 + 104xy$

9) $20(2x^2 - 8x - 5)$

$40x^2 - 160x - 100$

10) $3x(3x - 2)$

$9x^2 - 6x$

11) $6x^3(3x^2 - 2x + 2)$

$18x^5 - 12x^4 + 12x^3$

12) $8x^2(3x^2 - 5xy + 7y^2)$

$24x^4 - 40x^2y + 56xy^2$

13) $2x^2(3x^2 - 5x + 12)$

$6x^4 - 10x^3 + 24x$

14) $2x^3(2x^2 + 5x - 4)$

$4x^5 + 10x^4 - 8x^3$

15) $5x(6x^2 - 5xy + 2y^2)$

$30x^2 - 25x^2y + 10xy^2$

16) $9(x^2 + xy - 8y^2)$

$9x^2 + 9xy - 72y^2$

Multiplying Binomials

Helpful	Use "FOIL". (First–Out–In–Last)	**Example:**
Hints	$(x + a)(x + b) = x^2 + (b + a)x + ab$	$(x + 2)(x - 3) =$ $x^2 - x - 6$

✎**Multiply.**

1) $(3x - 2)(4x + 2)$

2) $(2x - 5)(x + 7)$

3) $(x + 2)(x + 8)$

4) $(x^2 + 2)(x^2 - 2)$

5) $(x - 2)(x + 4)$

6) $(x - 8)(2x + 8)$

7) $(5x - 4)(3x + 3)$

8) $(x - 7)(x - 6)$

9) $(6x + 9)(4x + 9)$

10) $(2x - 6)(5x + 6)$

11) $(x - 7)(x + 7)$

12) $(x + 4)(4x - 8)$

13) $(6x - 4)(6x + 4)$

14) $(x - 7)(x + 2)$

15) $(x - 8)(x + 8)$

16) $(3x + 3)(3x - 4)$

17) $(x + 3)(x + 3)$

18) $(x + 4)(x + 6)$

Factoring Trinomials

Helpful	"FOIL"	Example:
	$(x + a)(x + b) = x^2 + (b + a)x + ab$	$x^2 + 5x + 6 =$
Hints	"Difference of Squares"	$(x + 2)(x + 3)$
	$a^2 - b^2 = (a + b)(a - b)$	
	$a^2 + 2ab + b^2 = (a + b)(a + b)$	
	$a^2 - 2ab + b^2 = (a - b)(a - b)$	
	"Reverse FOIL"	
	$x^2 + (b + a)x + ab = (x + a)(x + b)$	

✍ *Factor each trinomial.*

1) $x^2 - 7x + 12$

2) $x^2 + 5x - 14$

3) $x^2 - 11x - 42$

4) $6x^2 + x - 12$

5) $x^2 - 17x + 30$

6) $x^2 + 8x + 15$

7) $3x^2 + 11x - 4$

8) $x^2 - 6x - 27$

9) $10x^2 + 33x - 7$

10) $x^2 + 24x + 144$

11) $49x^2 + 28xy + 4y^2$

12) $16x^2 - 40x + 25$

13) $x^2 - 10x + 25$

14) $25x^2 - 20x + 4$

15) $x^3 + 6x^2y^2 + 9xy^3$

16) $9x^2 + 24x + 16$

17) $x^2 - 8x + 16$

18) $x^2 + 121 + 22x$

Operations with Polynomials

Helpful	– When multiplying a monomial by a polynomial, use the distributive property.	**Example:**
Hints	$a \times (b + c) = a \times b + a \times c$	$5(6x - 1) =$ $30x - 5$

✍️ Find each product.

1) $3x^2 (6x - 5)$

2) $5x^2 (7x - 2)$

3) $-3 (8x - 3)$

4) $6x^3 (-3x + 4)$

5) $9 (6x + 2)$

6) $8 (3x + 7)$

7) $5 (6x - 1)$

8) $-7x^4 (2x - 4)$

9) $8 (x^2 + 2x - 3)$

10) $4 (4x^2 - 2x + 1)$

11) $2 (3x^2 + 2x - 2)$

12) $8x (5x^2 + 3x + 8)$

13) $(9x + 1) (3x - 1)$

14) $(4x + 5) (6x - 5)$

15) $(7x + 3) (5x - 6)$

16) $(3x - 4) (3x + 8)$

Answers of Worksheets – Chapter 9

Classifying Polynomials

1) Linear monomial

2) Quartic monomial

3) Linear binomial

4) Constant monomial

5) Linear binomial

6) Cubic binomial

7) Quantic monomial

8) Linear binomial

9) Quadratic binomial

10) Seventh degree binomial

11) Quartic polynomial with four terms

12) Quartic polynomial with four terms

13) Sixth degree trinomial

14) Quadratic trinomial

15) Sixth degree binomial

16) Seventh degree polynomial with four terms

17) Sixth degree trinomial

18) Quartic trinomial

Writing Polynomials in Standard Form

1) $-5x^3 + 3x^2$

2) $4x^3$

3) $-6x^3 + 2x^2 + x$

4) $2x$

5) $9x^4 - 7x + 12$

6) $-2x^3 + 5x^2 + 13x$

7) -3

8) $3x^2 + 10x - 8$

9) $x^2 + 3x - 10$

10) $-2x^2 - x + 12$

11) $9x^5 - x^3$

12) $-6x^3 + 6x^2 + 15x$

13) $11x^6 + 22x^4$

14) $x^2 + 9x + 18$

15) $x^2 + 8x + 16$

16) $24x^2 - 5x - 14$

17) $15x^3 + 10x^2 + 5x$

18) $42x^4 - 7x^2 + 21x$

Simplifying Polynomials

1) $-7x^3 - x^2 + 14$

2) $-x^3 + 8x^2$

3) $3x^6 - 162$

4) $-6x^3 + 24x^2 + 17$

5) $-12x^3 - x^2 + 33$

6) $3x^3 + 2x^2 - 12x$

7) $9x^2 - 36x + 32$

8) $144x^2 + 48xy + 4y^2$

9) $12x^2 + 4x + 2$

10) $6x - 1$

11) $3x^3 - 1$

12) $x^2 - 8x + 15$

13) $9x^2 - 64$

14) $16x^2 - 8x + 5$

Adding and Subtracting Polynomials

1) $4x^3$

2) $6x^3 - 2$

3) $4x^2 - 5$

4) $-x^2 + 2x$

5) $4x$

6) $6x^4 - 8x$

7) $-12x^3 + 6x$

8) $5x^3 - 13x^2$

9) $-4x^3 + 11x^2 - 6$

10) $2x^4 + 9x^3$

11) $33x^5 - 4x^4 + 16x^3$

12) $5x^5 + 23x^2 - 11x$

13) $12x^5 + 13x^4 - 3x^2 + 8$

14) $3x^5 + 10x^4 - 3x^3 + x^2 - 11$

Multiplying Monomials

1) $8xy^2z^3$

2) $4x^3y^2$

3) $-8p^5q^4$

4) $8s^5t^7$

5) $-36p^7$

6) $-24p^3q^5r^4$

7) $96a^{10}b$

8) $-21u^6v^5$

9) $-8u^4$

10) $-18x^3y^3$

11) $-12y^4z^4$

12) $10a^3b^2c^4$

Multiplying and Dividing Monomials

1) $28x^7y^{10}$

2) $45x^{13}$

3) $84x^{11}y^{21}$

4) $8x^6y^2$

5) $19x^9y^5$

6) $5y$

7) $-5x^{11}y^4$

8) $-8x^5y^3$

Multiplying a Polynomial and a Monomial

1) $15x - 30y$

2) $18x^2 + 36xy$

3) $56x^2 - 32x$

4) $36x^2 + 108x$

5) $22x^2 - 121xy$

6) $12x^2 - 12xy$

7) $6x^3 - 9x^2 + 24x$

8) $52x^2 + 104xy$

9) $40x^2 - 160x - 100$

10) $9x^2 - 6x$

11) $18x^5 - 12x^4 + 12x^3$

12) $24x^4 - 40x^3y + 56y^2x^2$

13) $6x^4 - 10x^3 + 24x^2$

14) $4x^5 + 10x^4 - 8x^3$

15) $30x^3 - 25x^2y + 10xy^2$

16) $9x^2 + 9xy - 72y^2$

Multiplying Binomials

1) $12x^2 - 2x - 4$

2) $2x^2 + 9x - 35$

3) $x^2 + 10x + 16$

4) $x^4 - 4$

5) $x^2 + 2x - 8$

6) $2x^2 - 8x - 64$

7) $15x^2 + 3x - 12$

8) $x^2 - 13x + 42$

9) $24x^2 + 90x + 81$

10) $10x^2 - 18x - 36$

11) $x^2 - 49$

12) $4x^2 + 8x - 32$

13) $36x^2 - 16$

14) $x^2 - 5x - 14$

15) $x^2 - 64$

16) $9x^2 - 3x - 12$

17) $x^2 + 6x + 9$

18) $x^2 + 10x + 24$

Factoring Trinomials

1) $(x - 3)(x - 4)$

2) $(x - 2)(x + 7)$

3) $(x + 3)(x - 14)$

4) $(2x + 3)(3x - 4)$

5) $(x - 15)(x - 2)$

6) $(x + 3)(x + 5)$

7) $(3x - 1)(x + 4)$

8) $(x - 9)(x + 3)$

9) $(5x - 1)(2x + 7)$

10) $(x + 12)(x + 12)$

11) $(7x + 2y)(7x + 2y)$

12) $(4x - 5)(4x - 5)$

13) $(x - 5)(x - 5)$

14) $(5x - 2)(5x - 2)$

15) $x(x^2 + 6xy^2 + 9y^3)$

16) $(3x + 4)(3x + 4)$

17) $(x - 4)(x - 4)$

18) $(x + 11)(x + 11)$

Operations with Polynomials

1) $18x^3 - 15x^2$

2) $35x^3 - 10x^2$

3) $-24x + 9$

4) $-18x^4 + 24x^3$

5) $54x + 18$

6) $24x + 56$

7) $30x - 5$

8) $-14x^5 + 28x^4$

9) $8x^2 + 16x - 24$

10) $16x^2 - 8x + 4$

11) $6x^2 + 4x - 4$

12) $40x^3 + 24x^2 + 64x$

13) $27x^2 - 6x - 1$

14) $24x^2 + 10x - 25$

15) $35x^2 - 27x - 18$

16) $9x^2 + 12x - 32$

Chapter 10: Quadratic and System of Equations

Topics that you'll learn in this chapter:

- ✓ Solve a Quadratic Equation
- ✓ Solving Systems of Equations by Substitution
- ✓ Solving Systems of Equations by Elimination
- ✓ Systems of Equations Word Problems

Mathematics is the door and key to the sciences. — Roger Bacon

Solve a Quadratic Equation

Helpful	Write the equation in the form of	Example:
	$ax^2 + bx + c = 0$	$x^2 + 5x + 6 = 0$
	Factorize the quadratic.	$(x + 3)(x + 2) = 0$
Hints	Use quadratic formula if you couldn't factorize the quadratic.	$(x + 3) = 0$
		$x = -3$
	Quadratic formula	$x + 2 = 0$
	$$x = \frac{-b \pm \sqrt{b^2 - 4ac}}{2a}$$	$x = -2$

✎ **Solve each equation.**

1) $(x + 2)(x - 4) = 0$

2) $(x + 5)(x + 8) = 0$

3) $(3x + 2)(x + 3) = 0$

4) $(4x + 7)(2x + 5) = 0$

5) $x^2 - 11x + 19 = -5$

6) $x^2 + 7x + 18 = 8$

7) $x^2 - 10x + 22 = -2$

8) $x^2 + 3x - 12 = 6$

9) $18x^2 + 45x - 27 = 0$

10) $90x^2 - 84x = -18$

11) $x^2 + 8x = -15$

Solving Systems of Equations by Substitution

Helpful Hints	Consider the system of equations $x - y = 1, -2x + y = 6$ Substitute x = 1 – y in the second equation $-2(1 - y) + y = 5 \qquad y = 2$ Substitute $y = 2$ in $x = 1 + y$ $x = 1 + 2 = 3$	**Example:** $-2x - 2y = -13$ $-4x + 2y = 10$ $(0.5, 6)$

Solve each system of equation by substitution.

1) $-2x + 2y = 4$

$-2x + y = 3$

5) $3x - 9y = -3$

$3y = 3x - 3$

2) $-10x + 2y = -6$

$6x - 16y = 48$

6) $-4x + 12y = 12$

$-14x + 16y = -10$

3) $y = -8$

$16x - 12y = 72$

7) $x + 20y = 20$

$x + 15y = 5$

4) $2y = -6x + 10$

$10x - 8y = -6$

8) $2x + 8y = 28$

$x - 2y = 5$

Solving Systems of Equations by Elimination

Helpful	-	The elimination method for solving systems of linear equations uses the addition property of equality. You can add the same value to each side of an equation.	**Example:** $x + 2y = 6$ $+\ -x + y = 3$ $\overline{\qquad\qquad}$ $3y = 9$ $y = 3$ $x + 6 = 6$ $x = 0$
Hints			

Solve each system of equation by elimination.

1) $10x - 9y = -12$

   $-5x + 3y = 6$

2) $-3x - 4y = 5$

   $x - 2y = 5$

3) $5x - 14y = 22$

   $-6x + 7y = 3$

4) $10x - 14y = -4$

   $-10x - 20y = -30$

5) $32x + 14y = 52$

   $16x - 4y = -40$

6) $2x - 8y = -6$

   $8x + 2y = 10$

7) $-4x + 4y = -4$

   $4x + 2y = 10$

8) $4x + 6y = 10$

   $8x + 12y = -20$

Systems of Equations Word Problems

Helpful	Define your variables, Write two equations, and use one of the methods for solving systems of equations to solve.
Hints	

Example:

The difference of two numbers is 6. Their sum is 14. Find the numbers.

$x + y = 6$

$x + y = 14$ $(10, 4)$

1) A farmhouse shelters 10 animals, some are pigs and some are ducks. Altogether there are 36 legs. How many of each animal are there?

2) A class 0f 195 students went on a field trip. They took vehicles, some cars and some buses. Find the number of cars and the number of buses they took if each car holds 5 students and each bus hold 45 students.

3) The sum of the digits of a certain two–digit number is 7. Reversing its increasing the number by 9. What is the number?

4) A boat traveled 336 miles downstream and back. The trip downstream took 12 hours. The trip back took 14 hours. What is the speed of the boat in still water? What is the speed of the current?

Answers of Worksheets – Chapter 10

Solving Quadratic Equations

1) $x = -2, x = 4$

2) $x = -5, x = -8$

3) $x = -\dfrac{2}{3}, x = -3$

4) $x = -\dfrac{7}{4}, x = -\dfrac{5}{2}$

5) $x = 8, x = 3$

6) $x = -5, x = -2$

7) $x = 6, x = 4$

8) $x = -6, x = 3$

9) $x = \dfrac{1}{2}, x = -3$

10) $x = \dfrac{3}{5}, x = \dfrac{1}{3}$

11) $x = -5, x = -3$

Solving Systems of Equations by Substitution

1) (−1, 1)

2) (0, −3)

3) (−4, −8)

4) (1, 2)

5) (2, 1)

6) (3, 2)

7) (-4, 3)

8) $(8, \dfrac{3}{2})$

Solving Systems of Equations by Elimination

12) (−1.2, 0)

13) (1, −2)

14) (−4, −3)

15) (1, 1)

16) (−1, 6)

17) (1, 1)

18) (2, 1)

19) No solution

Systems of Equations Word Problems

1) There are 8 pigs and 2 ducks.

2) There are 3 cars and 4 buses.

3) 10 and 4.

4) 34

5) 24 and 42

Chapter 11: Exponents and Radicals

Topics that you'll learn in this chapter:

- ✓ Multiplication Property of Exponents
- ✓ Division Property of Exponents
- ✓ Powers of Products and Quotients
- ✓ Zero and Negative Exponents
- ✓ Negative Exponents and Negative Bases
- ✓ Writing Scientific Notation
- ✓ Square Roots

Mathematics is no more computation than typing is literature.

— John Allen Paulos

Multiplication Property of Exponents

Helpful Hints	Exponents rules	Example:

Helpful

Hints

Exponents rules

$x^a \cdot x^b = x^{a+b}$ $\dfrac{x^a}{x^b} = x^{a-b}$

$\dfrac{1}{x^b} = x^{-b}$ $(x^a)^b = x^{a.b}$

$(xy)^a = x^a \cdot y^a$

Example:

$(x^2y)^3 = x^6y^3$

✎ *Simplify.*

1) $4^2 \cdot 4^2$

2) $2^1 \cdot 2^2 \cdot 2^2$

3) $3^2 \cdot 3^2$

4) $3x^3 \cdot x^1$

5) $12x^4 \cdot 3x$

6) $6x \cdot 2x^2$

7) $5x^4 \cdot 5x^4$

8) $6x^2 \cdot 6x^3y^4$

9) $7x^2y^5 \cdot 9xy^3$

10) $7xy^4 \cdot 4x^3y^3$

11) $(2x^2)^2$

12) $3x^5y^3 \cdot 8x^2y^3$

13) $7x^3 \cdot 10y^3x^5 \cdot 8yx^3$

14) $(x^4)^3$

15) $(2x^2)^4$

16) $(x^2)^3$

17) $(6x)^2$

18) $3x^4y^5 \cdot 7x^2y^3$

Division Property of Exponents

Helpful	$\dfrac{x^a}{x^b} = x^{a-b}$, $x \neq 0$	Example:
Hints		$\dfrac{x^{12}}{x^5} = x^7$

✎ Simplify.

1) $\dfrac{5^5}{5}$

2) $\dfrac{3}{3^5}$

3) $\dfrac{2^2}{2^3}$

4) $\dfrac{2^4}{2^2}$

5) $\dfrac{x}{x^3}$

6) $\dfrac{3x^3}{9x^4}$

7) $\dfrac{2x^{-5}}{9x^{-2}}$

8) $\dfrac{21x^8}{7x^3}$

9) $\dfrac{7x^6}{4x^7}$

10) $\dfrac{6x^2}{4x^3}$

11) $\dfrac{5x}{10x^3}$

12) $\dfrac{3x^3}{2x^5}$

13) $\dfrac{12x^3}{14x^6}$

14) $\dfrac{12x^3}{9y^8}$

15) $\dfrac{25xy^4}{5x^6y^2}$

16) $\dfrac{2x^4}{7x}$

17) $\dfrac{16x^2y^8}{4x^3}$

18) $\dfrac{12x^4}{15x^7y^9}$

19) $\dfrac{12yx^4}{10yx^8}$

20) $\dfrac{16x^4y}{9x^8y^2}$

21) $\dfrac{5x^8}{20x^8}$

Powers of Products and Quotients

Helpful	For any nonzero numbers a and b and any integer x, $(ab)^x = a^x \cdot b^x$.	**Example:**
Hints		$(2x^2 \cdot y^3)^2 =$
		$4x^2 \cdot y^6$

$Log_5 25 = x \qquad 5^x = 25$

$+ = 2$

Simplify.

1) $(2x^3)^4$

$16x^{12}$

2) $(4xy^4)^2$

$16x^2 \cdot 8$

3) $(5x^4)^2$

$25x^8$

4) $(11x^5)^2$

$121x^{10}$

5) $(4x^2y^4)^4$

$256x^8 \cdot y$

6) $(2x^4y^4)^3$

7) $(3x^2y^2)^2$

$9x^4y^4$

8) $(3x^4y^3)^4$

$81x^{16}y^{12}$

9) $(2x^6y^8)^2$

$4x^{42}y^{16}$

10) $(12x \cdot 3x)^3$

$1,728 \times 27 = 46,656$

11) $(2x^9 \cdot x^6)^3$

12) $(5x^{10}y^3)^3$

13) $(4x^3 \cdot x^2)^2$

14) $(3x^3 \cdot 5x)^2$

15) $(10x^{11}y^3)^2$

16) $(9x^7 y^5)^2$

17) $(4x^4y^6)^5$

18) $(4x^4)^2$

19) $(3x \cdot 4y^3)^2$

20) $(9x^2y)^3$

21) $(12x^2y^5)^2$

Zero and Negative Exponents

Helpful	A negative exponent simply means that the base is on the wrong side of the fraction line, so you need to flip the base to the other side. For instance, "x^{-2}" (pronounced as "ecks to the minus two") just means "x^2" but underneath, as in $\frac{1}{x^2}$	**Example:** $5^{-2} = \frac{1}{25}$
Hints		

✎**Evaluate the following expressions.**

1) 8^{-2}

2) 2^{-4}

3) 10^{-2}

4) 5^{-3}

5) 22^{-1}

6) 9^{-1}

7) 3^{-2}

8) 4^{-2}

9) 5^{-2}

10) 35^{-1}

11) 6^{-3}

12) 0^{15}

13) 10^{-9}

14) 3^{-4}

15) 5^{-2}

16) 2^{-3}

17) 3^{-3}

18) 8^{-1}

19) 7^{-3}

20) 6^{-2}

21) $(\frac{2}{3})^{-2}$

22) $(\frac{1}{5})^{-3}$

23) $(\frac{1}{2})^{-8}$

24) $(\frac{2}{5})^{-3}$

Negative Exponents and Negative Bases

Helpful *Hints*	– Make the power positive. A negative exponent is the reciprocal of that number with a positive exponent. **Example:** – The parenthesis is important! $2x^{-3} = \frac{2}{x^3}$ -5^{-2} is not the same as $(-5)^{-2}$ $-5^{-2} = -\frac{1}{5^2}$ and $(-5)^{-2} = +\frac{1}{5^2}$

✎ *Simplify.*

1) -6^{-1}

2) $-4x^{-3}$

3) $-\dfrac{5x}{x^{-3}}$

4) $-\dfrac{a^{-3}}{b^{-2}}$

5) $-\dfrac{5}{x^{-3}}$

6) $\dfrac{7b}{-9c^{-4}}$

7) $-\dfrac{5n^{-2}}{10p^{-3}}$

8) $\dfrac{4ab^{-2}}{-3c^{-2}}$

9) $-12x^2y^{-3}$

10) $\left(-\dfrac{1}{3}\right)^{-2}$

11) $\left(-\dfrac{3}{4}\right)^{-2}$

12) $\left(\dfrac{3a}{2c}\right)^{-2}$

13) $\left(-\dfrac{5x}{3yz}\right)^{-3}$

14) $-\dfrac{2x}{a^{-4}}$

Writing Scientific Notation

Helpful	– It is used to write very big or very small numbers in decimal form.

– In scientific notation all numbers are written in the form of:

$$m \times 10^n$$

Decimal notation	Scientific notation
5	5×10^0
−25,000	$−2.5 \times 10^4$
0.5	5×10^{-1}
2,122.456	$2,122456 \times 10^3$

✍ Write each number in scientific notation.

1) 91×10^3

2) 60

3) 2000000

4) 0.0000006

5) 354000

6) 0.000325

7) 2.5

8) 0.00023

9) 56000000

10) 2000000

11) 78000000

12) 0.0000022

13) 0.00012

14) 0.004

15) 78

16) 1600

17) 1450

18) 130000

19) 60

20) 0.113

21) 0.02

Square Roots

Helpful	— A square root of x is a number r whose square is: $r^2 = x$	**Example:**
	r is a square root of x.	$\sqrt{4} = 2$
Hints		

✍ *Find the value each square root.*

1) $\sqrt{1}$

2) $\sqrt{4}$

3) $\sqrt{9}$

4) $\sqrt{25}$

5) $\sqrt{16}$

6) $\sqrt{49}$

7) $\sqrt{36}$

8) $\sqrt{0}$

9) $\sqrt{64}$

10) $\sqrt{81}$

11) $\sqrt{121}$

12) $\sqrt{225}$

13) $\sqrt{144}$

14) $\sqrt{100}$

15) $\sqrt{256}$

16) $\sqrt{289}$

17) $\sqrt{324}$

18) $\sqrt{400}$

19) $\sqrt{900}$

20) $\sqrt{529}$

21) $\sqrt{90}$

Answers of Worksheets – Chapter 11

Multiplication Property of Exponents

1) 4^4

2) 2^5

3) 3^4

4) $3x^4$

5) $36x^5$

6) $12x^3$

7) $25x^8$

8) $36x^5y^4$

9) $63x^3y^8$

10) $28x^4y^7$

11) $4x^4$

12) $24x^7y^6$

13) $560x^{11}y^4$

14) x^{12}

15) $16x^8$

16) x^6

17) $36x^2$

18) $21x^6y^8$

Division Property of Exponents

1) 5^4

2) $\dfrac{1}{3^4}$

3) $\dfrac{1}{2}$

4) 2^2

5) $\dfrac{1}{x^2}$

6) $\dfrac{1}{3x}$

7) $\dfrac{2}{9x^3}$

8) $3x^5$

9) $\dfrac{7}{4x}$

10) $\dfrac{3}{2x}$

11) $\dfrac{1}{2x^2}$

12) $\dfrac{3}{2x^2}$

13) $\dfrac{6}{7x^3}$

14) $\dfrac{4x^3}{3y^8}$

15) $\dfrac{5y^2}{x^5}$

16) $\dfrac{2x^3}{7}$

17) $\dfrac{4y^8}{x}$

18) $\dfrac{4}{5x^3y^9}$

19) $\dfrac{6}{5x^4}$

20) $\dfrac{16}{9x^4y}$

21) $\dfrac{1}{4}$

Powers of Products and Quotients

1) $16x^{12}$

2) $16x^2y^8$

3) $25x^8$

4) $121x^{10}$

5) $256x^8y^{16}$

6) $8x^{12}y^{12}$

7) $9x^4y^4$

8) $81x^{16}y^{12}$

9) $4x^{12}y^{16}$

10) $46,656x^6$

11) $8x^{45}$

12) $125x^{30}y^9$

13) $16x^{10}$

14) $225x^8$

15) $100x^{22}y^6$

16) $81x^{14}y^{10}$

17) $1,024x^{20}y^{30}$

18) $16x^8$

19) $144x^2y^6$ 20) $729x^6y^3$ 21) $144x^4y^{10}$

Zero and Negative Exponents

1) $\frac{1}{64}$

2) $\frac{1}{16}$

3) $\frac{1}{100}$

4) $\frac{1}{125}$

5) $\frac{1}{22}$

6) $\frac{1}{9}$

7) $\frac{1}{9}$

8) $\frac{1}{16}$

9) $\frac{1}{25}$

10) $\frac{1}{35}$

11) $\frac{1}{216}$

12) 0

13) $\frac{1}{1000000000}$

14) $\frac{1}{81}$

15) $\frac{1}{25}$

16) $\frac{1}{8}$

17) $\frac{1}{27}$

18) $\frac{1}{8}$

19) $\frac{1}{343}$

20) $\frac{1}{36}$

21) $\frac{9}{4}$

22) 125

23) 256

24) $\frac{125}{8}$

Negative Exponents and Negative Bases

1) $-\frac{1}{6}$

2) $-\frac{4}{x^3}$

3) $-5x^4$

4) $-\frac{b^2}{a^3}$

5) $-5x^3$

6) $-\frac{7bc^4}{9}$

7) $-\frac{p^3}{2n^2}$

8) $-\frac{4ac^2}{3b^2}$

9) $-\frac{12x^2}{y^3}$

10) 9

11) $\frac{16}{9}$

12) $\frac{4c^2}{9a^2}$

13) $-\frac{27y^3z^3}{125x^3}$

14) $-2xa^4$

Writing Scientific Notation

1) 9.1×10^4

2) 6×10^1

3) 2×10^6

4) 6×10^{-7}

5) 3.54×10^5

6) 3.25×10^{-4}

7) 2.5×10^0

8) 2.3×10^{-4}

9) 5.6×10^7

10) 2×10^6

11) 7.8×10^7

12) 2.2×10^{-6}

13) 1.2×10^{-4}

14) 4×10^{-3}

15) 7.8×10^1

16) 1.6×10^3

18) 1.3×10^5

20) 1.13×10^{-1}

17) 1.45×10^3

19) 6×10^1

21) 2×10^{-2}

Square Roots

1) 1

8) 0

15) 16

2) 2

9) 8

16) 17

3) 3

10) 9

17) 18

4) 5

11) 11

18) 20

5) 4

12) 15

19) 30

6) 7

13) 12

20) 23

7) 6

14) 10

21) $3\sqrt{10}$

Chapter 12: Geometry

Topics that you'll learn in this chapter:

✓ The Pythagorean Theorem

✓ Area of Triangles

✓ Perimeter of Polygons

✓ Area and Circumference of Circles

✓ Area of Squares, Rectangles, and Parallelograms

✓ Area of Trapezoids

Mathematics is, as it were, a sensuous logic, and relates to philosophy as do the arts, music, and plastic art to poetry. —

K, Shegel

The Pythagorean Theorem

Helpful

Hints

– In any right triangle:

$a^2 + b^2 = c^2$

Example:

Missing side = 6

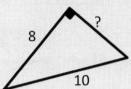

8

?

10

✍ Do the following lengths form a right triangle?

1)

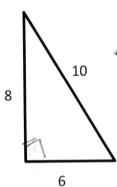

8

10

6

✓

2)

3

4

5

✓

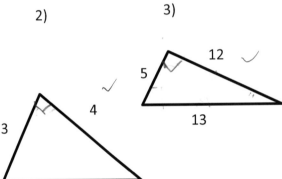

3)

5

12

13

✓

✍ Find each missing length to the nearest tenth.

4)

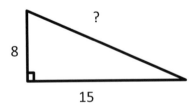

8

?

15

5)

24

?

10

6)

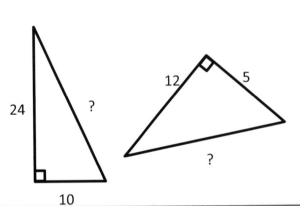

12

5

?

Area of Triangles

Helpful $Area = \frac{1}{2} \ (base \ \times height)$

Hints

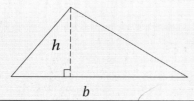

🖎 **Find the area of each.**

1)

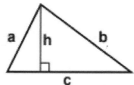

c = 9 mi

h = 3.7 mi

$\frac{1}{2} (9_{mi} \times 3.7_{mi})$. 𝑜

16.65 mi

2)

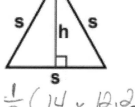

s = 14 m

h = 12.2 m

$\frac{1}{2} (14_m \times 12.2_m)$

85.4 mi

3)

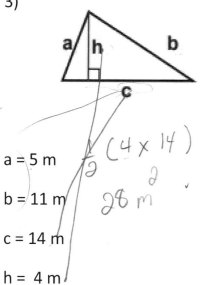

a = 5 m

b = 11 m

c = 14 m

h = 4 m

$\frac{1}{2} (4 \times 14)$

28 m²

4)

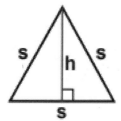

s = 10 m

h = 8.6 m

$\frac{1}{2} (8.6 \times 10)$

43 m²

Perimeter of Polygons

Helpful

Hints

Perimeter of a square = 4s

 s

Perimeter of a rectangle

= 2($l + w$)

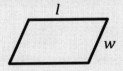 w

l

Perimeter of trapezoid

= a + b + c + d

a
d   b
c

Perimeter of Pentagon = 6a

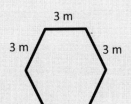 a

Perimeter of a parallelogram = 2(l + w)

l

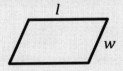 w

Example:

P = 18

3 m

3 m   3 m

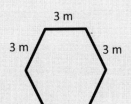

✎ **Find the perimeter of each shape.**

1)

5 m

5 m   5 m

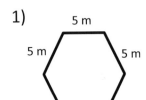

2)

15 mm

15 mm   15mm

15 mm

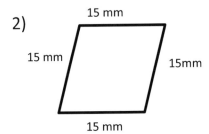

3)

12 ft   12 ft

12 ft   12 ft

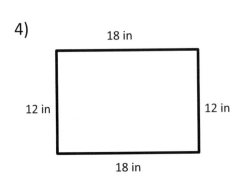

4)

18 in

12 in   12 in

18 in

Area and Circumference of Circles

Helpful Hints	Area = πr² Circumference = 2πr 	Example: If the radius of a circle is 3, then: Area = 28.27 Circumference = 18.85

✎ **Find the area and circumference of each.** (π = 3.14)

1)

4 in

2)

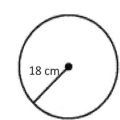

18 cm

3)

5 m

4)

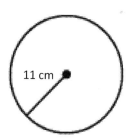

11 cm

5)

8 km

6)

21 in

Area of Squares, Rectangles, and Parallelograms

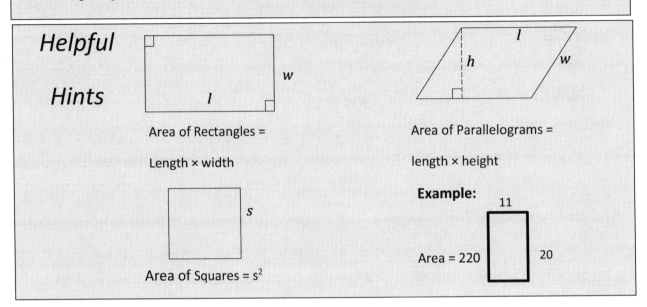

Helpful

Hints

Area of Rectangles =

Length × width

Area of Squares = s²

Area of Parallelograms =

length × height

Example:

Area = 220

✎ *Find the area of each.*

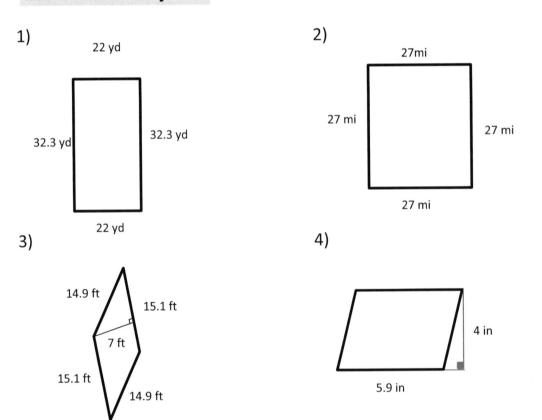

1)

22 yd

32.3 yd   32.3 yd

22 yd

2)

27mi

27 mi   27 mi

27 mi

3)

14.9 ft

15.1 ft

7 ft

15.1 ft

14.9 ft

4)

4 in

5.9 in

Area of Trapezoids

Helpful

$A = \frac{1}{2}h(b_1 + b_2)$

Hints

Example:

$A = 252 \text{ cm}^2$

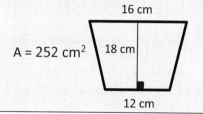

16 cm

18 cm

12 cm

✏️ **Calculate the area for each trapezoid.**

1)

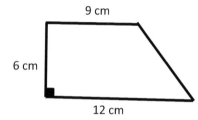

9 cm

6 cm

12 cm

2)

14 m

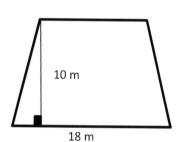

10 m

18 m

3)

22 mi

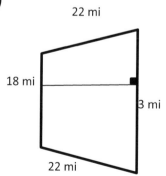

18 mi

3 mi

22 mi

4)

8.6 nm

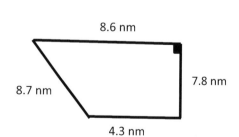

8.7 nm

7.8 nm

4.3 nm

Answers of Worksheets – Chapter 12

The Pythagorean Theorem

1) yes
2) yes
3) yes

4) 17
5) 26
6) 13

Area of Triangles

1) 16.65 mi^2
2) 85.4 m^2

3) 28 m^2
4) 43 m^2

Perimeter of Polygons

1) 30 m
2) 60 mm

3) 48 ft
4) 60 in

Area and Circumference of Circles

1) Area: 50.24 in^2, Circumference: 25.12 in
2) Area: 1,017.36 cm^2, Circumference: 113.04 cm
3) Area: 78.5m^2, Circumference: 31.4 m
4) Area: 379.94 cm^2, Circumference: 69.08 cm
5) Area: 200.96 km^2, Circumference: 50.2 km
6) Area: 1,384.74 km^2, Circumference: 131.88 km

Area of Squares, Rectangles, and Parallelograms

1) 710.6 yd^2
2) 729 mi^2

3) 105.7 ft^2
4) 23.6 in^2

Area of Trapezoids

1) 63 cm^2
2) 160 m^2

3) 410 mi^2
4) 50.31 nm^2

Chapter 13: Solid Figures

Topics that you'll learn in this chapter:

- ✓ Volume of Cubes
- ✓ Volume of Rectangle Prisms
- ✓ Surface Area of Cubes
- ✓ Surface Area of Rectangle Prisms
- ✓ Volume of a Cylinder
- ✓ Surface Area of a Cylinder

Mathematics is a great motivator for all humans. Because its career starts with zero and it never end (infinity)

Volume of Cubes

Helpful	– Volume is the measure of the amount of space inside of a solid figure, like a cube, ball, cylinder or pyramid.
Hints	– Volume of a cube = (one side)^3
	– Volume of a rectangle prism: Length × Width × Height

✍ **Find the volume of each.**

1)

2)

3)

4)
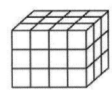

5)
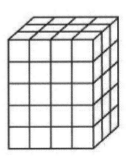

6)
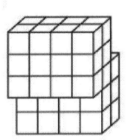

Volume of Rectangle Prisms

Helpful

Hints

Volume of rectangle prism

length × width × height

Example:

$10 \times 5 \times 8 = 400m^3$

10 m

8 m

5 m

✎ **Find the volume of each of the rectangular prisms.**

1)

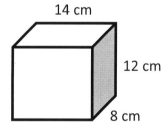

14 cm

12 cm

8 cm

2)

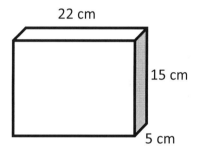

22 cm

15 cm

5 cm

3)

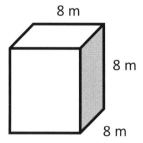

8 m

8 m

8 m

4)

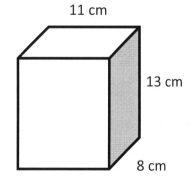

11 cm

13 cm

8 cm

Surface Area of Cubes

Helpful	Surface Area of a cube =	**Example:**

Surface Area of a cube =

6 × (one side of the cube)²

Helpful

Hints

Example:

6 × 4² = 96m²

📐 *Find the surface of each cube.*

1)

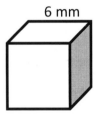

6 mm

2)

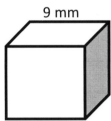

9 mm

3)

10 cm

4)

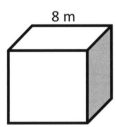

8 m

5)

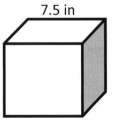

7.5 in

6)

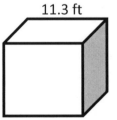

11.3 ft

Surface Area of a Rectangle Prism

Helpful

Hints

Surface Area of a Rectangle Prism Formula:

SA =2 [(width × length) + (height × length) + width × height)]

✎ **Find the surface of each prism.**

1)

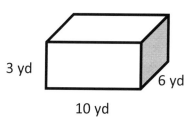

3 yd
6 yd
10 yd

2)

7 mm

7 mm

7 mm

3)

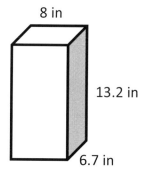

8 in

13.2 in

6.7 in

4)

17 cm

17 cm

11 cm

Volume of a Cylinder

Helpful

Hints

Volume of Cylinder Formula = π(radius)² × height

π = 3.14

🖎*Find the volume of each cylinder.* (π = 3.14)

1)

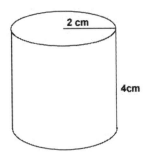

2)

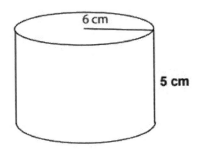

3)

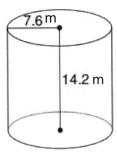

4)

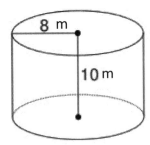

Surface Area of a Cylinder

Helpful		**Example:**
Hints	Surface area of a cylinder $SA = 2\pi r^2 + 2\pi rh$	Surface area = 1727

14 m
11 m

✏️ **Find the surface of each cylinder.** ($\pi = 3.14$)

1)

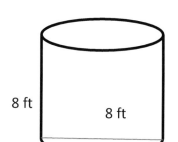

8 ft   8 ft

2)

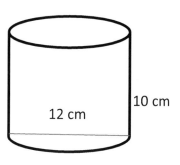

12 cm   10 cm

3)

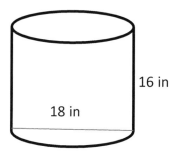

18 in   16 in

4)

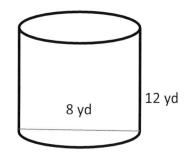

8 yd   12 yd

Answers of Worksheets – Chapter 13

Volumes of Cubes

1) 8

2) 4

3) 5

4) 36

5) 60

6) 44

Volume of Rectangle Prisms

1) 1344 cm^3

2) 1650 cm^3

3) 512 m^3

4) 1144 cm^3

Surface Area of a Cube

1) 216 mm^2

2) 486 mm^2

3) 600 cm^2

4) 384 m^2

5) 337.5 in^2

6) 766.14 ft^2

Surface Area of a Prism

1) 216 yd^2

2) 294 mm^2

3) 495.28 in^2

4) 1326 cm^2

Volume of a Cylinder

1) 50.24 cm^3

2) 565.2 cm^3

3) 2,575.403 m^3

4) 2009.6 m^3

Surface Area of a Cylinder

1) 301.44 ft^2

2) 602.88 cm^2

3) 1413 in^2

4) 401.92 yd^2

Chapter 14: Functions Operations

Topics that you'll learn in this chapter:

- ✓ Relations and Functions
- ✓ Function Notation
- ✓ Adding and Subtracting Functions
- ✓ Multiplying and Dividing Functions

Millions saw the apple fall, but Newton asked why." – Bernard Baruch

Function Notation

Helpful *Hints*	Function notation is the way a function is written. It is meant to be a precise way of giving information about the function without a rather lengthy written explanation. The most popular function notation is $f(x)$ which is read "f of x".	**Example:** $f = 12x$ $f(x)\ 12x$

✎ **Write in function notation.**

1) d = $22t$

2) c = $p^2 + 5p + 5$

3) $m = 25n - 120$

4) $y = 2x - 6$

✎ **Evaluate each function.**

5) w$(x) = 3x + 1$, find $w(4)$

6) $h(n) = n^2 - 10$, find $h(5)$

7) $h(x) = x^3 + 8$, find $h(-2)$

8) $h(n) = -2n^2 - 6n$, find $h(2)$

9) $g(n) = 3n^2 + 2n$, find $g(2)$

10) $g(n) = 10n - 3$, find $g(6)$

11) $g(n) = 8n + 4$, find $g(1)$

12) $h(x) = 4x - 22$, find $h(2)$

13) $h(a) = -11a + 5$, find $h(2a)$

14) $k(a) = 7a + 3$, find $k(a - 2)$

15) $h(x) = 3x + 5$, find $h(6x)$

16) $h(x) = x^2 + 1$, find $h(\frac{x}{4})$

Adding and Subtracting Functions

Helpful

Hints

Just like we can add and subtract numbers, we can add and subtract functions. For example, if we had functions f and g, we could create two new functions: $f + g$ and $f - g$.

Example:

$f(x) = 12x$

$g(x) = x^2 + 3x$

$(f + g)(x) = f(x) + g(x) =$

$12x + x^2 + 3x$

$x^2 + 15x$

✎ *Perform the indicated operation.*

1) $h(t) = 2t + 1$

    $g(t) = 2t + 2$

    Find $(h - g)(t)$

2) $g(a) = -3^a - 3$

    f(a) = $a^2 + 5$

    Find $(g - f)(a)$

3) $g(x) = 2x - 5$

    $h(x) = 4x + 5$

    Find $g(3) - h(3)$

4) $h(3) = 3x + 3$

    $g(x) = -4x + 1$

    Find $(h + g)(10)$

5) $f(x) = 4x - 3$

    $g(x) = x^3 + 2x$

    Find $(f - g)(4)$

6) $h(n) = 4n + 5$

    $g(n) = 3n + 4$

    Find $(h - g)(n)$

7) $g(x) = -x^2 - 1 - 2x$

    $f(x) = 5 + x$

    Find $(g - f)(x)$

8) $g(t) = 2t + 5$

    $f(t) = -t^2 + 5$

    Find $(g + f)(t)$

Multiplying and Dividing Functions

Helpful Hints

Just like we can multiply and divide numbers, we can multiply and divide functions. For example, if we had functions f and g, we could create two new functions

$$f \cdot g, \text{ and } \frac{f}{g}.$$

Example:

$f(x) = 2x$

$g(x) = x^2 + x$

$(f \cdot g)(x) =$

$f(x) \cdot g(x) =$

$2x^3 + 2x^2$

✎ **Perform the indicated operation.**

1) $g(a) = 2a - 1$

$h(a) = 3a - 3$

Find $(g \cdot h)(-4)$

2) $f(x) = 2x^3 - 5x^2$

$g(x) = 2x - 1$

Find $(f \cdot g)(x)$

3) $g(t) = t^2 + 3$

$h(t) = 4t - 3$

Find $(g \cdot h)(-1)$

4) $g(n) = n^2 + 4 + 2n$

$h(n) = -3n + 2$

Find $(g \cdot h)(1)$

5) $g(a) = 3a + 2$

$f(a) = 2a - 4$

Find $(\frac{g}{f})(3)$

6) $f(x) = 3x - 1$

$g(x) = x^2 - x$

Find $(\frac{f}{g})(x)$

Find $(\frac{h}{g})(a)$

7) $h(a) = 3a$

$g(a) = -a^3 - 3$

Answers of Worksheets – Chapter 14

Function Notation

1) $d(t) = 22t$
2) $c(p) = p^2 + 5p + 5$
3) $m(n) = 25n - 120$
4) $f(x) = 2x - 6$
5) 13
6) 15
7) 0
8) −20
9) 16
10) 57
11) 12
12) −8
13) $-22a + 5$
14) $7a - 11$
15) $18x + 5$
16) $1 + \frac{1}{16}x^2$

Adding and Subtracting Functions

1) −1
2) $-a^2 - 3a - 8$
3) −16
4) −6
5) −59
6) $n + 1$
7) $-x^2 - 3x - 6$
8) $-t^2 + 2t + 10$

Multiplying and Dividing Functions

1) 135
2) $4x^4 - 12x^3 + 5x^2$
3) −28
4) −7
5) $\frac{11}{2}$
6) $\frac{3x-1}{x^2-x}$
7) $\frac{3a}{-a^2-3}$

Chapter 15: Statistics and Probability

Topics that you'll learn in this chapter:

- ✓ Mean, Median, Mode, and Range of the Given Data
- ✓ The Pie Graph or Circle Graph
- ✓ Probability
- ✓ Factorials
- ✓ Permutations
- ✓ Combination

Mathematics is no more computation than typing is literature.

– John Allen Paulos

Mean, Median, Mode, and Range of the Given Data

Helpful	- Mean: $\dfrac{\text{sum of the data}}{\text{of data entires}}$	Example:
	- Mode: value in the list that appears most often	22, 16, 12, 9, 7, 6, 4, 6
Hints	- Range: largest value – smallest value	Mean = 10.25
		Mod = 6
		Range = 18

✎ **Find Mean, Median, Mode, and Range of the Given Data.**

1) 7, 2, 5, 1, 1, 2

2) 2, 2, 2, 3, 6, 3, 7, 4

3) 9, 4, 3, 1, 7, 9, 4, 6, 4

4) 8, 4, 2, 4, 3, 2, 4, 5

5) 8, 5, 7, 5, 7, 9, 8

6) 5, 1, 4, 4, 9, 2, 9, 2, 5, 1

7) 4, 1, 5, 9, 7, 7, 5, 4, 3, 5

8) 7, 5, 4, 9, 6, 7, 7, 5, 2

9) 2, 5, 5, 6, 2, 4, 7, 6, 4, 9

10) 10, 5, 2, 5, 4, 5, 8, 10

11) 5, 1, 5, 2, 2

12) 2, 3, 5, 9, 6

The Pie Graph or Circle Graph

Helpful	A Pie Chart is a circle chart divided into sectors, each sector represents the relative size of each value.
Hints	

The circle graph below shows all Jason's expenses for last month. Jason spent $300 on his bills last month.

Answer following questions based on the Pie graph.

Jason's monthly expenses

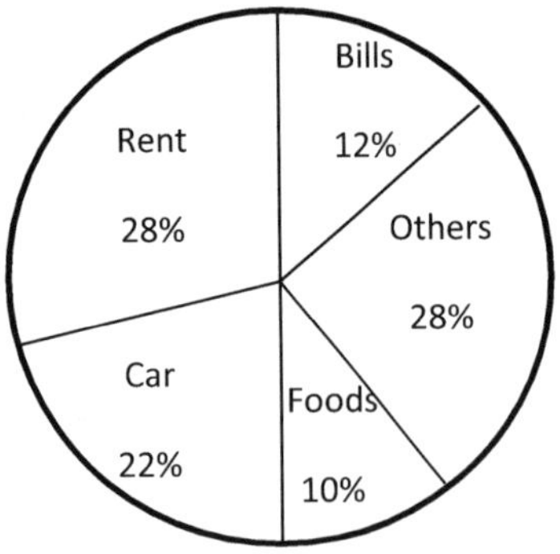

1- How much did Jason spend on his car last month?

2- How much did Jason spend for foods last month?

3- How much did Jason spend on his rent last month?

4- What fraction is Jason's expenses for his bills and Car out of his total expenses last month?

5- How much was Jason's senses last month?

Probability of Simple Events

Helpful	-	Probability is the likelihood of something happening in the future. It is expressed as a number between zero (can never happen) to 1 (will always happen).	**Example:**
Hints	-	Probability can be expressed as a fraction, a decimal, or a percent.	Probability of a flipped coins turns up 'heads' Is $0.5 = \dfrac{1}{2}$

✏ Solve.

1) A number is chosen at random from 1 to 10. Find the probability of selecting a 4 or smaller.

2) There are 135 blue balls and 15 red balls in a basket. What is the probability of randomly choosing a red ball from the basket?

3) A number is chosen at random from 1 to 10. Find the probability of selecting of 4 and factors of 6.

4) What is the probability of choosing a Hearts in a deck of cards? (A deck of cards contains 52 cards)

5) A number is chosen at random from 1 to 50. Find the probability of selecting prime numbers.

6) A number is chosen at random from 1 to 25. Find the probability of not selecting a composite number.

Factorials

Helpful	Factorials means to multiply a series of descending natural numbers.	**Example:**
Hints		$4! = 4 \times 3 \times 2 \times 1$

✎**Determine the value for each expression.**

1) $\dfrac{9!}{6!}$

2) $\dfrac{8!}{5!}$

3) $\dfrac{7!}{5!}$

4) $\dfrac{20!}{18!}$

5) $\dfrac{22!}{18!5!}$

6) $\dfrac{10!}{8!2!}$

7) $\dfrac{100!}{97!}$

8) $\dfrac{14!}{10!4!}$

9) $\dfrac{10!}{8!}$

10) $\dfrac{25!}{20!}$

11) $\dfrac{14!}{9!3!}$

12) $\dfrac{55!}{53!}$

13) $\dfrac{(2.3)!}{3!}$

14) $5! + 4!$

Permutations

| Helpful

Hints | The number of ways to choose a sample of r elements from a set of n distinct objects where order does matter, and replacements are not allowed.

$$_nP_k = \frac{n!}{(n-k)!}$$ | **Example:**

$$_4P_2 = \frac{4!}{(4-2)!}$$

$$= 12$$ |

✎**Evaluate each expression.**

1) $_4P_2$

2) $_5P_1$

3) $_6P_2$

4) $_6P_6$

5) $-4 + {_7P_4}$

6) $5 \cdot {_6P_5}$

7) $_7P_2$

8) $_4P_1$

9) $_8P_5$

10) $_7P_3$

11) How many possible 7–digit telephone numbers are there?

12) When order does matter, how many ways can one choose 8 out of 12 cards?

Combination

Helpful Hints	The number of ways to choose a sample of r elements from a set of n distinct objects where order does not matter, and replacements are not allowed. $_nC_r = \dfrac{n!}{r!\,(n-r)!}$	**Example:** $_4C_2 = \dfrac{4!}{2!(4-2)!}$ $= 3$

✎ List all possible combinations.

1) 4, 5, 6

2) T, V, W, taken two at a time

✎ Evaluate each expression.

3) $_7C_5$

4) $_4C_2$

5) $_9C_3$

6) $_5C_2$

7) $_{12}C_8$

8) $_9C_6$

9) $_{22}C_{20}$

10) $_{12}C_9$

11) $_{11}C_8$

12) $_{25}C_{23}$

13) $_{17}C_{10}$

14) $_{24}C_5$

15) $4 \cdot {}_{18}C_{14}$

16) $_{20}C_{16}$

Answers of Worksheets – Chapter 15

Mean, Median, Mode, and Range of the Given Data

1) mean: 3, median: 2, mode: 1, 2, range: 6
2) mean: 3.625, median: 3, mode: 2, range: 5
3) mean: 5.22, median: 4, mode: 4, range: 8
4) mean: 4, median: 4, mode: 4, range: 6
5) mean: 7, median: 7, mode: 5, 7, 8, range: 4
6) mean: 4.2, median: 4, mode: 1,2,4,5,9, range: 8
7) mean: 5, median: 5, mode: 5, range: 8
8) mean: 5.78, median: 6, mode: 7, range: 7
9) mean: 5, median: 5, mode: 2, 4, 5, 6, range: 7
10) mean: 6.125, median: 5, mode: 5, range: 8
11) mean: 3, median: 2, mode: 2, 5, range: 4
12) mean: 5, median: 5, mode: none, range: 7

The Pie Graph or Circle Graph

1) $550
2) $250
3) $700
4) $\frac{17}{50}$
5) $2500

Probability of simple events

1) $\frac{2}{5}$
2) $\frac{1}{10}$
3) $\frac{1}{5}$
4) $\frac{1}{4}$
5) $\frac{3}{10}$
1) $\frac{2}{5}$

Factorials

1) 504
2) 336
3) 42
4) 380
5) 1,463
6) 45
7) 970,200
8) 1,001
9) 90
10) 6,375,600
11) 40,040
12) 2,970
13) 120
14) 144

Permutations

1) 12	5) 206	9) 336
2) 5	6) 30	10) 840
3) 30	7) 42	11) 9×10^6
4) 1	8) 4	12) 11,880

Combination

1) 456, 465, 546, 564, 645, 654	6) 10	12) 300
2) TV VW TW	7) 495	13) 19,448
3) 21	8) 84	14) 42,504
4) 6	9) 231	15) 12,240
5) 84	10) 220	16) 4, 845
	11) 165	

TASC Test Review

The Test Assessing Secondary Completion, commonly known as the TASC or high school equivalency degree, is a standardized test. The TASC is a standardized test to verify that examinees have knowledge in core content areas equivalent to that of graduating high school seniors.

There are five subject area tests on TASC:

- o Reading;
- o Writing;
- o Social Studies;
- o Science;
- o Mathematics.

The TASC Mathematics test is a 105-minute test that covers basic mathematics topics, quantitative problem-solving and algebraic questions. There are two Mathematics sections on the TASC. The first section contains 40 multiple choice questions where calculators are permitted. You have 50 minutes to complete this section. The second section contains 12 Gridded-Response questions. Calculator is NOT allowed in the second part. Test takers have 55 minutes to answer all questions in this section. Examinees will also be given a page of mathematic formulas to use during the test.

In this book, we have covered all Mathematics topics you need to know. Now, it's time to take a real TASC test. In this section, there are two complete TASC Mathematics Tests. Take these tests to see what score you'll be able to receive on a real TASC test.

Good luck!

TASC Mathematics
Practice Tests

Time to Test

Time to refine your quantitative reasoning skill with a practice test

In this section, there are two complete TASCT Mathematics practice tests. Take these tests to simulate the test day experience. After you've finished, score your tests using the answer keys.

Before You Start

- You'll need a pencil, a calculator and a timer to take the test.

- For each question, there are four possible answers. Choose which one is best.

- It's okay to guess. There is no penalty for wrong answers.

- Use the answer sheet provided to record your answers.

- After you've finished the test, review the answer key to see where you went wrong.

Good Luck!

Mathematics is like love; a simple idea, but it can get complicated.

TASC Practice Tests Answer Sheet

Remove (or photocopy) these answer sheets and use them to complete the practice tests.

TASC Practice Test 1 – Section 1 Answer Sheet

1 Ⓐ Ⓑ Ⓒ Ⓓ	9 Ⓐ Ⓑ Ⓒ Ⓓ	17 Ⓐ Ⓑ Ⓒ Ⓓ	25 Ⓐ Ⓑ Ⓒ Ⓓ	33 Ⓐ Ⓑ Ⓒ Ⓓ
2 Ⓐ Ⓑ Ⓒ Ⓓ	10 Ⓐ Ⓑ Ⓒ Ⓓ	18 Ⓐ Ⓑ Ⓒ Ⓓ	26 Ⓐ Ⓑ Ⓒ Ⓓ	34 Ⓐ Ⓑ Ⓒ Ⓓ
3 Ⓐ Ⓑ Ⓒ Ⓓ	11 Ⓐ Ⓑ Ⓒ Ⓓ	19 Ⓐ Ⓑ Ⓒ Ⓓ	27 Ⓐ Ⓑ Ⓒ Ⓓ	35 Ⓐ Ⓑ Ⓒ Ⓓ
4 Ⓐ Ⓑ Ⓒ Ⓓ	12 Ⓐ Ⓑ Ⓒ Ⓓ	20 Ⓐ Ⓑ Ⓒ Ⓓ	28 Ⓐ Ⓑ Ⓒ Ⓓ	36 Ⓐ Ⓑ Ⓒ Ⓓ
5 Ⓐ Ⓑ Ⓒ Ⓓ	13 Ⓐ Ⓑ Ⓒ Ⓓ	21 Ⓐ Ⓑ Ⓒ Ⓓ	29 Ⓐ Ⓑ Ⓒ Ⓓ	37 Ⓐ Ⓑ Ⓒ Ⓓ
6 Ⓐ Ⓑ Ⓒ Ⓓ	14 Ⓐ Ⓑ Ⓒ Ⓓ	22 Ⓐ Ⓑ Ⓒ Ⓓ	30 Ⓐ Ⓑ Ⓒ Ⓓ	38 Ⓐ Ⓑ Ⓒ Ⓓ
7 Ⓐ Ⓑ Ⓒ Ⓓ	15 Ⓐ Ⓑ Ⓒ Ⓓ	23 Ⓐ Ⓑ Ⓒ Ⓓ	31 Ⓐ Ⓑ Ⓒ Ⓓ	39 Ⓐ Ⓑ Ⓒ Ⓓ
8 Ⓐ Ⓑ Ⓒ Ⓓ	16 Ⓐ Ⓑ Ⓒ Ⓓ	24 Ⓐ Ⓑ Ⓒ Ⓓ	32 Ⓐ Ⓑ Ⓒ Ⓓ	40 Ⓐ Ⓑ Ⓒ Ⓓ

TASC Practice Test 1: Section 2: Grid-ins Questions

41

42

43

44

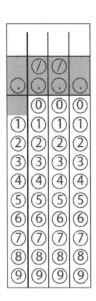
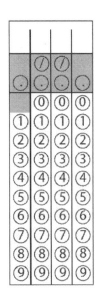
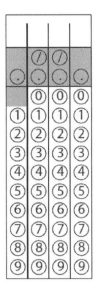

45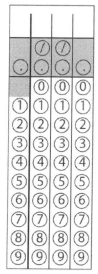

46

47

48

49

50

51

52

TASC Practice Test 2 – Section 1 Answer Sheet

1	Ⓐ Ⓑ Ⓒ Ⓓ	9	Ⓐ Ⓑ Ⓒ Ⓓ	17	Ⓐ Ⓑ Ⓒ Ⓓ	25	Ⓐ Ⓑ Ⓒ Ⓓ	33	Ⓐ Ⓑ Ⓒ Ⓓ
2	Ⓐ Ⓑ Ⓒ Ⓓ	10	Ⓐ Ⓑ Ⓒ Ⓓ	18	Ⓐ Ⓑ Ⓒ Ⓓ	26	Ⓐ Ⓑ Ⓒ Ⓓ	34	Ⓐ Ⓑ Ⓒ Ⓓ
3	Ⓐ Ⓑ Ⓒ Ⓓ	11	Ⓐ Ⓑ Ⓒ Ⓓ	19	Ⓐ Ⓑ Ⓒ Ⓓ	27	Ⓐ Ⓑ Ⓒ Ⓓ	35	Ⓐ Ⓑ Ⓒ Ⓓ
4	Ⓐ Ⓑ Ⓒ Ⓓ	12	Ⓐ Ⓑ Ⓒ Ⓓ	20	Ⓐ Ⓑ Ⓒ Ⓓ	28	Ⓐ Ⓑ Ⓒ Ⓓ	36	Ⓐ Ⓑ Ⓒ Ⓓ
5	Ⓐ Ⓑ Ⓒ Ⓓ	13	Ⓐ Ⓑ Ⓒ Ⓓ	21	Ⓐ Ⓑ Ⓒ Ⓓ	29	Ⓐ Ⓑ Ⓒ Ⓓ	37	Ⓐ Ⓑ Ⓒ Ⓓ
6	Ⓐ Ⓑ Ⓒ Ⓓ	14	Ⓐ Ⓑ Ⓒ Ⓓ	22	Ⓐ Ⓑ Ⓒ Ⓓ	30	Ⓐ Ⓑ Ⓒ Ⓓ	38	Ⓐ Ⓑ Ⓒ Ⓓ
7	Ⓐ Ⓑ Ⓒ Ⓓ	15	Ⓐ Ⓑ Ⓒ Ⓓ	23	Ⓐ Ⓑ Ⓒ Ⓓ	31	Ⓐ Ⓑ Ⓒ Ⓓ	39	Ⓐ Ⓑ Ⓒ Ⓓ
8	Ⓐ Ⓑ Ⓒ Ⓓ	16	Ⓐ Ⓑ Ⓒ Ⓓ	24	Ⓐ Ⓑ Ⓒ Ⓓ	32	Ⓐ Ⓑ Ⓒ Ⓓ	40	Ⓐ Ⓑ Ⓒ Ⓓ

TASC Practice Test 2: Section 2: Grid-ins Questions

41   42   43   44

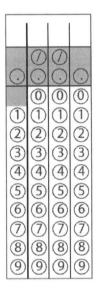

45

46

47

48

49

50

51

52

TASC Mathematics
Practice Test 1

Section 1

(Calculator)

40 questions

Total time for this section: 50 Minutes

You may use a calculator on this Section.

Mathematics Reference Sheet

Cylinder: $v = \pi r^2 h$

Pyramid: $v = \frac{1}{3} bh$

cone: $v = \frac{1}{3} \pi r^2 h$

Sphere: $\frac{4}{3} \pi r^3$

coordinate Geometry

Midpoint of the segment AB:

$$M\left(\frac{x_1 + x_2}{2}, \frac{y_1 + y_2}{2}\right)$$

Distance from A to B:

$$d = \sqrt{(x_1 - x_2)^2 + (y_1 - y_2)^2}$$

Slope of a line:

$$m = \frac{y_2 - y_1}{x_2 - x_1} = \frac{rise}{run}$$

Special Factoring

$a^2 - b^2 = (a + b)(a - b)$

$a^2 + 2ab + b^2 = (a + b)(a + b)$

$a^2 - 2ab + b^2 = (a - b)(a - b)$

$a^3 + b^3 = (a + b)(a^2 - ab + b^2)$

$a^3 - b^3 = (a - b)(a^2 + ab + b^2)$

Quadratic Formula

for $ax^2 + bx + c = 0$

$$x = \frac{-b \pm \sqrt{b^2 - 4ac}}{2a}$$

Interest

Simple Interest:

$$I = prt$$

Interest Formula (compounded n times per year):

$$A = p\left(1 + \frac{r}{n}\right)^{nt}$$

A = Amount after t years.

p = principal

r = annual interest rate

t = time in years

I = Interest

Trigonometric Identities

Pythagorean Theorem: $a^2 + b^2 = c^2$

$\sin \theta = \frac{opp}{hyp}$

$\cos \theta = \frac{adj}{hyp}$

$\tan \theta = \frac{opp}{adj}$

$sin^2\theta + cos^2\theta = 1$

$$Density = \frac{Mass}{Volume}$$

Central Angle	Inscribed Angle	Intersecting Chords Theorem
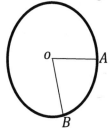	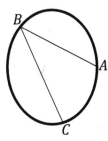	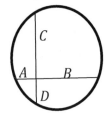
$m\angle AOB = m\widehat{AB}$	$m\angle ABC = \frac{1}{2}m\,\widehat{AC}$	$A \cdot B = C \cdot D$

Probability

Permutations: $_nP_r = \dfrac{n!}{(n-r)!}$

Combinations: $_nC_r = \dfrac{n!}{(n-r)!\,r!}$

Multiplication rule (independent events): P(A and B) = P(A)·P(B)

Multiplication rule (general): P(A and B) = P(A)·P(B|A)

Addition rule: P(A or B) = P(A) + P(B) − P(A and B)

Conditional Probability: P(B|A) = $\dfrac{P(A\ and\ B)}{P(A)}$

Arithmetic Sequence: $a_n = a_1 + (n-1)d$ where a_n is the nth term, a_1 is the first term, and d is the common difference.

Geometric Sequence: $a_n = a_1 r^{(n-1)}$ where a_n is the nth term, a_1 is the first term, and r is the common ratio.

1) When a number is subtracted from 24 and the difference is divided by that number, the result is 3. What is the value of the number?

   A. 2

   B. 4

   C. 6

   D. 12

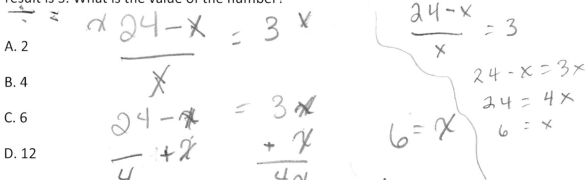

2) An angle is equal to one ninth of its supplement. What is the measure of that angle?

   A. 18

   B. 24

   C. 36

   D. 45

3) John traveled 150 km in 6 hours and Alice traveled 180 km in 4 hours. What is the ratio of the average speed of John to average speed of Alice?

   A. 3 : 2

   B. 2 : 3

   C. 5 : 9

   D. 5 : 6

4) A taxi driver earns $9 per 1-hour work. If he works 10 hours a day and in 1 hour he uses 2-liters petrol with price $1 for 1-liter. How much money does he earn in one day?

A. $90

B. $88

C. $70

D. $60

Handwritten work: earns $9/hr $\frac{\$9}{hr} \times 10hr = \$90$ earns $\frac{2 \text{ liter}}{hr} \cdot 10hrs = 20L$ exp $\$\frac{1}{Liter} \cdot 20L = \$20$ expenes $90 - 20 = 70$

5) Find the average of the following numbers: 17, 13, 7, 21, 22

A. 17

B. 16.5

C. 16

D. 11

6) The price of a sofa is decreased by 15% to $476. What was its original price?

A. $480

B. $520

C. $560

D. $600

Handwritten work: $Px \cdot .85 = 476$ Orig $\times (1 - $ sale % $) = $ sale price $\frac{Px \cdot .85}{.85} = \frac{476}{.85} = 560$

7) Right triangle ABC has two legs of lengths 9 cm (AB) and 12 cm (AC). What is the length of the third side (BC)?

A. 6 cm

B. 8 cm

C. 14 cm

D. 15 cm

Handwritten work: $a^2 + b^2 = c^2$ $9^2 + 12^2 = c^2$ $81 + 144 = 225 = c^2$ $\sqrt{225} = 15$

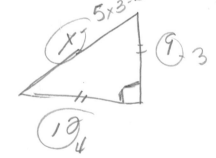

8) If 40% of a class are girls, and 25% of girls play tennis, what percent of the class play tennis?

(handwritten: 40% girls · 25% Tennis)

A. 10%

(handwritten: .4 × .25 = .1 or 10%)

B. 15%

C. 20%

(handwritten: 10%)

D. 40%

9) The area of a circle is less than 64 π. Which of the following can be the circumference of the circle? (Select one or more answer choices)

(handwritten: $\Pi = 3.14$ Find r Circumference then $C = \Pi d$)

A. 12 π

B. 16 π

(handwritten: $\Pi = \frac{22}{7}$)

C. 24 π

(handwritten: $A = \Pi r^2 < 64\Pi$ $r < 8$)

(handwritten: if $r < 8$ $2r < 16$ $C < \Pi 16$)

D. 32 π

(handwritten: $C = 2\Pi r = 16\Pi$ Since $r < 8$ C is less than 16Π)

10) Which of the following values for x and y satisfy the following system of equations?

$$\begin{cases} x + 4y = 10 \\ 5x + 10y = 20 \end{cases}$$

(handwritten:
$-5x - 20y = 50$
$5x + 10y = 20$
———————
$\frac{-10y}{10} = \frac{30}{-10}$
$y = -3$ *)*

A. $x = 3, y = 2$

B. $x = 2, y - 3$

C. $x = -2, y = 3$

D. $x = 3, y = -2$

11) If 60% of A is 20% of B, then B is what percent of A?

$A = B$

B is 100% of A

A. 3%

$\dfrac{0.60\ A}{0.80} = \dfrac{0.20\ B}{0.80}$

$3A = B$

B. 30%

300%

C. 200%

$3\ A = B$

D. 300%

12) The price of a car was $20,000 in 2014, $16,000 in 2015 and $12,800 in 2016. What is the rate of <u>depreciation</u> of the price of car per year?

$\dfrac{\%\ \text{change}}{\text{the original price}}$

A. 15%

$2014 - 2014$

B. 20%

$\dfrac{4000}{20,000}\quad \dfrac{4}{20} = \dfrac{1}{5} = 20\%$

C. 25%

$\dfrac{3200}{16,000} = \dfrac{32}{160} = \dfrac{2}{10} : 20\%$

D. 30%

$2014 \to 2015$

$2015 - 2016$

13) The width of a box is one third of its length. The height of the box is one third of its width. If the length of the box is 27 cm, what is the volume of the box?

Volume = Length × Width × Heigh

A. 81 cm³

$w = \dfrac{1}{3} L$, if $L = 27$, $w = 9$

B. 162 cm³

$H = \dfrac{1}{3} w = \dfrac{1}{3}(9) = 3$

C. 243 cm³

D. 729 cm³

14) How many possible outfit combinations come from six shirts, three slacks, and five ties?

$6 \times 3 \times 5 = 90$

A. 15

B. 18

C. 30

D. 90

15) A bank is offering 4.5% simple interest on a savings account. If you deposit $8,000, how much interest will you earn in five years?

A. $360

$$8,000 \times 0.045 \times 5$$

B. $720

C. $1,800

D. $3,600

16) What is the value of 6^4 ?

A. 216

$$6 \times 6 \cdot 6 \cdot 6$$

B. 1,296

C. 7,776

D. 46,656

17) 25 is What percent of 20?

A. 20%

B. 25%

C. 125%

D. 150%

18) If the area of trapezoid is 126 cm, what is the perimeter of the trapezoid?

A. 12 cm

B. 32 cm

C. 46 cm

D. 55 cm

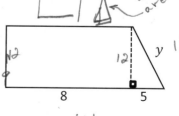

area rect = 8x
area tri = 2.5x
10.5x

$8x + 2.5x = 126$

$\dfrac{10.5x}{10.5} = \dfrac{126}{10.5}$

$x = 12$

$12^2 + 5^2 = x = 16$

$y = 13$

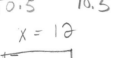

$p = 8 + 12 + 8 + 5 + 13 = 46$

3:4:5
5:12:13

19) In five successive hours, a car travels 40 km, 45 km, 50 km, 35 km and 55 km. In the next five hours, it travels with an average speed of 50 km per hour. Find the total distance the car traveled in 10 hours.

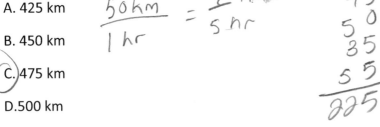

A. 425 km

B. 450 km

C. 475 km

D. 500 km

20) How long does a 420–miles trip take moving at 50 miles per hour (mph)?

A. 4 hours

B. 6 hours and 24 minutes

C. 8 hours and 24 minutes

D. 8 hours and 30 minutes

21) In the xy-plane, the point $(4,3)$ and $(3,2)$ are on line A. Which of the following points could also be on line A? (Select one or more answer choices)

A. $(-1, 2)$

B. $(5, 7)$

C. $(3, 4)$

D. $(-1, -2)$

22) Two third of 18 is equal to $\frac{2}{5}$ of what number?

A. 12

B. 20

C. 30

D. 60

23) The marked price of a computer is D dollar. Its price decreased by 20% in January and later increased by 10 % in February. What is the final price of the computer in D dollar?

A. 0.80 D

B. 0.88 D

C. 0.90 D

D. 1.20 D

24) A $40 shirt now selling for $28 is discounted by what percent?

A. 20%

B. 30%

C. 40%

D. 60%

25) Which of the following could be the product of two consecutive prime numbers?

A. 2

B. 10

C. 14

D. 15

26) Which of the following lists shows the fractions in order from least to greatest?

$$\frac{3}{4}, \frac{2}{7}, \frac{3}{8}, \frac{5}{11}$$

A. $\frac{3}{8}, \frac{2}{7}, \frac{3}{4}, \frac{5}{11}$

B. $\frac{2}{7}, \frac{5}{11}, \frac{3}{8}, \frac{3}{4}$

C. $\frac{2}{7}, \frac{3}{8}, \frac{5}{11}, \frac{3}{4}$

D. $\frac{3}{8}, \frac{2}{7}, \frac{5}{11}, \frac{3}{4}$

27) A boat sails 40 miles south and then 30 miles east. How far is the boat from its start point?

    A. 45 miles

    B. 50 miles

    C. 60 miles

    D. 70 miles

28) The ratio of boys and girls in a class is 4:7. If there are 44 students in the class, how many more boys should be enrolled to make the ratio 1:1?

    A. 8

    B. 10

    C. 12

    D. 16

29) Sophia purchased a sofa for $530.40. The sofa is regularly priced at $624. What was the percent discount Sophia received on the sofa?

    A. 12%

    B. 15%

    C. 20%

    D. 25%

30) The score of Emma was half as that of Ava and the score of Mia was twice that of Ava. If the score of Mia was 60, what is the score of Emma?

    A. 12

    B. 15

    C. 20

    D. 30

31) A bag contains 18 balls: two green, five black, eight blue, a brown, a red and one white. If 17 balls are removed from the bag at random, what is the probability that a brown ball has been removed?

A. $\dfrac{1}{9}$

B. $\dfrac{1}{6}$

C. $\dfrac{16}{17}$

D. $\dfrac{17}{18}$

32) The average of five consecutive numbers is 38. What is the smallest number?

A. 38

B. 36

C. 34

D. 12

33) How many tiles of 8 cm^2 is needed to cover a floor of dimension 6 cm by 24 cm?

A. 6

B. 12

C. 18

D. 24

34) A rope weighs 600 grams per meter of length. What is the weight in kilograms of 12.2 meters of this rope? (1 kilograms = 1000 grams)

    A. 0.0732

    B. 0.732

    C. 7.32

    D. 73.20

35) A chemical solution contains 4% alcohol. If there is 24 ml of alcohol, what is the volume of the solution?

    A. 240 ml

    B. 480 ml

    C. 600 ml

    D. 1200 ml

36) The average weight of 18 girls in a class is 60 kg and the average weight of 32 boys in the same class is 62 kg. What is the average weight of all the 50 students in that class?

    A. 60

    B. 61.28

    C. 61.68

    D. 62.90

37) The price of a laptop is decreased by 10% to $360. What is its original price?

    A. 320

    B. 380

    C. 400

    D. 450

38) What is the median of these numbers? 4, 9, 13, 8, 15, 18, 5

    A. 8

    B. 9

    C. 13

    D. 15

39) The surface area of a cylinder is $150\pi\ cm^2$. If its height is 10 cm, what is the radius of the cylinder?

    A. 13 cm

    B. 11 cm

    C. 15 cm

    D. 5 cm

40) In 1999, the average worker's income increased $2,000 per year starting from $24,000 annual salary. Which equation represents income greater than average? (I = income, x = number of years after 1999)

    A. $I > 2000\ x + 24000$

    B. $I > -2000\ x + 24000$

    C. $I < -2000\ x + 24000$

    D. $I < 2000\ x - 24000$

IF YOU FINISH BEFORE TIME IS CALLED, YOU MAY CHECK YOUR WORK ON THIS SECTION ONLY. DO NOT TURN TO OTHER SECTION IN THE TEST. **STOP**

TASC Mathematics
Practice Test 1

Section 2

(No Calculator)

12 questions

Total time for this section: 55 Minutes

You may NOT use a calculator on this Section.

41) If $3x - 5 = 8.5$, What is the value of $5x + 3$?

42) What is the area of an isosceles right triangle that has one leg that measures 6?

43) The perimeter of the trapezoid below is 54. What is its area?

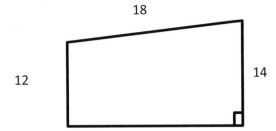

44) From last year, the price of gasoline has increased from $1.25 per gallon to $1.75 per gallon. The new price is what percent of the original price?

45) $-18 + 6 \times (-5) - [4 + 22 \times (-4)] \div 2 + 8 = ?$

46) A ladder leans against a wall forming a 60° angle between the ground and the ladder. If the bottom of the ladder is 45 feet away from the wall, how many feet is the ladder?

47) The volume of cube A is $\frac{1}{3}$ of its surface area. What is the length of an edge of cube A?

48) What is the value of $f(5)$ for the following function f?

$$f(x) = x^2 - 3x$$

49) If $\frac{x-3}{5} = N$ and $N = 6$, what is the value of x?

50) If the ratio of $5a$ to $2b$ is $\frac{1}{10}$, what is the ratio of a to b?

51) A construction company is building a wall. The company can build 30 cm of the wall per minute. After 40 minutes $\frac{3}{4}$ of the wall is completed. How many meters is the wall?

52) The average of 13, 15, 20 and x is 18. What is the value of x?

IF YOU FINISH BEFORE TIME IS CALLED, YOU MAY CHECK YOUR WORK ON THIS SECTION ONLY. DO NOT TURN TO OTHER SECTION IN THE TEST.   STOP

π
2
r

$C = \pi 2 r$

$A = \pi r^2$

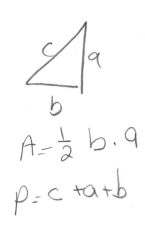

$A = \frac{1}{2} b \cdot a$

$p = c + a + b$

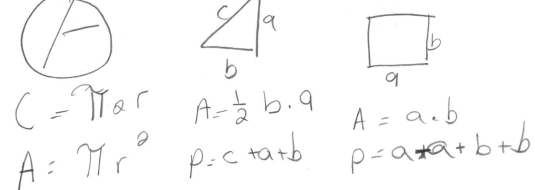

$A = a \cdot b$

$p = a \star a + b + b$

TASC Mathematics
Practice Test 2

Section 1

(Calculator)

40 questions

Total time for this section: 50 Minutes

You may use a calculator on this Section.

Mathematics Reference Sheet

Cylinder: $v = \pi r^2 h$

Pyramid: $v = \frac{1}{3} bh$

cone: $v = \frac{1}{3} \pi r^2 h$

Sphere: $\frac{4}{3} \pi r^3$

coordinate Geometry

Midpoint of the segment AB:

$$M\left(\frac{x_1+x_2}{2}, \frac{y_1+y_2}{2}\right)$$

Distance from A to B:

$$d = \sqrt{(x_1 - x_2)^2 + (y_1 - y_2)^2}$$

Slope of a line:

$$m = \frac{y_2 - y_1}{x_2 - x_1} = \frac{rise}{run}$$

Special Factoring
$a^2 - b^2 = (a + b)(a - b)$

$a^2 + 2ab + b^2 = (a + b)(a + b)$

$a^2 - 2ab + b^2 = (a - b)(a - b)$

$a^3 + b^3 = (a + b)(a^2 - ab + b^2)$

$a^3 - b^3 = (a - b)(a^2 + ab + b^2)$

Quadratic Formula
for $ax^2 + bx + c = 0$

$$x = \frac{-b \pm \sqrt{b^2 - 4ac}}{2a}$$

Interest
Simple Interest:
$$I = prt$$
Interest Formula (compounded n times per year):

$$A = p\left(1 + \frac{r}{n}\right)^{nt}$$

A = Amount after t years.

p = principal

r = annual interest rate

t = time in years

I = Interest

Trigonometric Identities

Pythagorean Theorem: $a^2 + b^2 = c^2$

$\sin \theta = \frac{opp}{hyp}$

$\cos \theta = \frac{adj}{hyp}$

$\tan \theta = \frac{opp}{adj}$

$sin^2\theta + cos^2\theta = 1$

$$\text{Density} = \frac{Mass}{Volume}$$

Central Angle	Inscribed Angle	Intersecting Chords Theorem
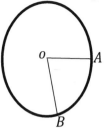	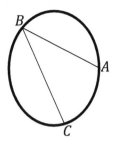	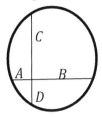
$m\angle AOB = m\widehat{AB}$	$m\angle ABC = \frac{1}{2} m\,\widehat{AC}$	$A \cdot B = C \cdot D$

Probability

Permutations: $_nP_r = \dfrac{n!}{(n-r)!}$

Combinations: $_nC_r = \dfrac{n!}{(n-r)!r!}$

Multiplication rule (independent events): P(A and B) = P(A)·P(B)

Multiplication rule (general): P(A and B) = P(A)·P(B|A)

Addition rule: P(A or B) = P(A) + P(B) − P(A and B)

Conditional Probability: P(B|A) = $\dfrac{P(A\ and\ B)}{P(A)}$

Arithmetic Sequence: $a_n = a_1 + (n-1)d$ where a_n is the nth term, a_1 is the first term, and d is the common difference.

Geometric Sequence: $a_n = a_1 r^{(n-1)}$ where a_n is the nth term, a_1 is the first term, and r is the common ratio.

1) What is the value of 3^6 ?

    A. 81

    B. 243

    C. 729

    D. 2,187

2) Simplify the expression.

$$(6x^3 - 8x^2 + 2x^4) - (4x^2 - 2x^4 + 2x^3)$$

    A. $4x^4 + 4x^3 - 12x^2$

$6x^3 - 8x^2 + 2x^4 \quad -4x^2 + 2x^4 - 2x^3$

    B. $4x^3 - 12x^2$

    C. $4x^4 + 4x^3 - 12x^2$

    D. $8x^3 - 12x^2$

3) In two successive years, the population of a town is increased by 15% and 20%. What percent of the population is increased after two years?

    A. 32%

    B. 35%

    C. 38%

    D. 68%

4) Which of the following graphs represents the compound inequality $-2 \leq 2x - 4 < 8$?

A.

B.

C.

(D.)

5) What is the volume of a box with the following dimensions?

Hight = 4 cm   Width = 5 cm   Length = 6 cm

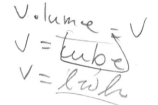

A. 15 cm³

B. 60 cm³

C. 90 cm³

(D.)120 cm³

6) Mr. Carlos family are choosing a menu for their reception. They have 3 choices of appetizers, 5 choices of entrees, 4 choices of cake. How many different menu combinations are possible for them to choose?

A. 12

B. 32

(C.)60

D. 120

7) In a stadium the ratio of home fans to visiting fans in a crowd is 5:7. Which of the following could be the total number of fans in the stadium?

A. 12,324 ÷ 12

B. 42,326 ÷ 12

C. 44,566 / 12

D. 66,812 / 12

$$\frac{5}{12} \qquad \frac{7}{12}$$

8) Last week 24,000 fans attended a football match. This week three times as many bought tickets, but one sixth of them cancelled their tickets. How many are attending this week?

A. 48,000

B. 54,000

C. 60,000

D. 72,000

9) What is the perimeter of a square in centimeters that has an area of 595.36 cm²?

A. 97.6
B. 96.2
C. 95.7
D. 92.6

$$\sqrt{x^2} = \sqrt{595.36}$$

$$x = 24.4 \times 4$$

10) Which of the following points lies on the line $x + 2y = 4$?

A. (−2, 3) (x, y)

B. (1, 2)

C. (−1, 3)

D. (−3, 4)

11) The perimeter of a rectangular yard is 60 meters. What is its length if its width is twice its length?

A. 10 meters

B. 18 meters

C. 20 meters

D. 24 meters

12) Which of the following shows the numbers in descending order?

$\frac{2}{3}$, 0.68 , 67% , $\frac{4}{5}$

A. 67%, 0.68, $\frac{2}{3}$, $\frac{4}{5}$

B. 67%, 0.68, $\frac{4}{5}$, $\frac{2}{3}$

C. 0.68, 67%, $\frac{2}{3}$, $\frac{4}{5}$

D. $\frac{2}{3}$, 67%, 0.68, $\frac{4}{5}$

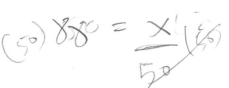

13) The mean of 50 test scores was calculated as 88. But, it turned out that one of the scores was misread as 94 but it was 69. What is the correct mean of the test scores?

A. 85

B. 87

C. 87.5

D. 88.5

14) Two dice are thrown simultaneously, what is the probability of getting a sum of 6 or 9?

    A. $\dfrac{1}{3}$

    B. $\dfrac{1}{4}$

    C. $\dfrac{1}{6}$

    D. $\dfrac{1}{12}$

15) A swimming pool holds 2,000 cubic feet of water. The swimming pool is 25 feet long and 10 feet wide. How deep is the swimming pool?

    A. 2

    B. 4

    C. 6

    D. 8

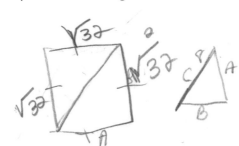

16) What is the area of a square whose diagonal is 8?

    A. 16

    B. 32

    C. 36

    D. 64

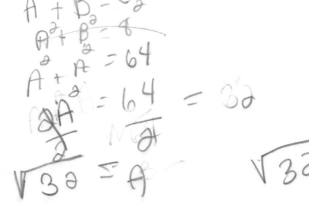

17) Anita's trick–or–treat bag contains 12 pieces of chocolate, 18 suckers, 18 pieces of gum, 24 pieces of licorice. If she randomly pulls a piece of candy from her bag, what is the probability of her pulling out a piece of sucker?

A. $\dfrac{1}{3}$

B. $\dfrac{1}{4}$

C. $\dfrac{1}{6}$

D. $\dfrac{1}{12}$

18) The average of 6 numbers is 12. The average of 4 of those numbers is 10. What is the average of the other two numbers.

A. 10

B. 12

C. 14

D. 16

19) 6. What is the value of x in the following system of equations?

$$2x + 5y = 11$$
$$4x - 2y = -14$$

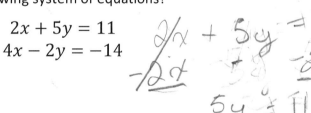

A. -1

B. 1

C. -2

D. 4

20) The perimeter of the trapezoid below is 36 cm. What is its area?

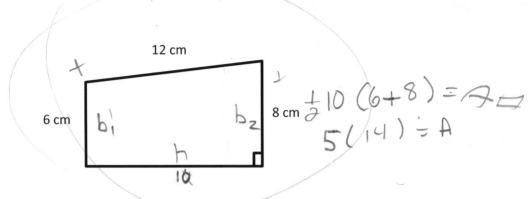

12 cm

6 cm

8 cm

A. 576 cm^2

B. 70 cm^2

C. 48 cm^2

D. 24 cm^2

$\frac{1}{2}10(6+8) = A = \Box$

$5(14) = A$

$\frac{1}{2}h(b_1 + b_2) = A$ Trapezoid

$6 + 12 + 8 + x = 36$

$26 + x = 36$

$-26 \quad -26$

$10 = x$

21) If 150 % of a number is 75, then what is the 90 % of that number?

A. 45

B. 50

C. 70

D. 85

22) A football team had $20,000 to spend on supplies. The team spent $14,000 on new balls. New sport shoes cost $120 each. Which of the following inequalities represent the number of new shoes the team can purchase.

A. $120x + 14,000 \leq 20,000$

B. $120x + 14,000 \geq 20,000$

C. $14,000x + 120 \leq 20,000$

D. $14,000x + 12,0 \geq 20,000$

23) A card is drawn at random from a standard 52–card deck, what is the probability that the card is of Hearts? (The deck includes 13 of each suit clubs, diamonds, hearts, and spades)

A. $\dfrac{1}{3}$

B. $\dfrac{1}{4}$

C. $\dfrac{1}{6}$

D. $\dfrac{1}{52}$

24) The average of five numbers is 24. If a sixth number that is greater than 42 is added, then, which of the following could be the new average? (Select one or more answer choices)

A. 25

B. 26

C. 27

D. 28

$2(L+W) = 36 \qquad L+W = 8$

25) The <u>length</u> of a rectangle is 3 meters greater than 4 times its width. The perimeter of the rectangle is 36 meters. What is the area of the rectangle in meters?

A. 35

B. 45

C. 55

D. 65

$L = 4W + 3 \qquad P = 36 \qquad 15 \times 3 =$

$2L + 2W = 36 \qquad L = 4(3) + 3 \quad \boxed{45}$

$2(4W+3) + 2W \qquad 10W = 30 \qquad 12 + 3$

$8W + 6 + 2W \qquad W = 3 \qquad L = 15$

26) The ratio of boys and girls in a class is 4:7. If there are 44 students in the class, how many more boys should be enrolled to make the ratio 1:1?

A. 8

B. 10

C. 12

D. 14

27) Mr. Jones saves $2,500 out of his monthly family income of $55,000. What fractional part of his income does he save?

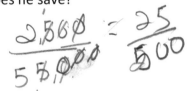

$\dfrac{2,500}{55,000} = \dfrac{25}{500}$

A. $\dfrac{1}{22}$

B. $\dfrac{1}{11}$

C. $\dfrac{3}{25}$

D. $\dfrac{2}{15}$

28) Jason needs an 75% average in his writing class to pass. On his first 4 exams, he earned scores of 68%, 72%, 85%, and 90%. What is the minimum score Jason can earn on his fifth and final test to pass?

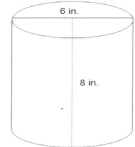
6 in.

8 in.

A. 375

B. 315

C. 90

D. 60

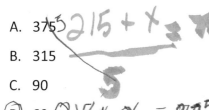

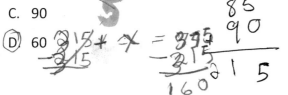

29) What is the value of x in the following equation?

$$\frac{2}{3}x + \frac{1}{6} = \frac{1}{3}$$

A. 6

B. $\frac{1}{2}$

C. $\frac{1}{3}$

D. $\frac{1}{4}$

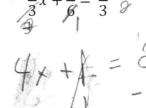

30) What is the surface area of the cylinder below?

A. 48 π in²

B. 57 π in²

C. 66 π in²

D. 288 π in²

31) The square of a number is $\frac{25}{64}$. What is the cube of that number?

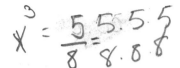

A. $\frac{5}{8}$

B. $\frac{25}{254}$

C. $\frac{125}{512}$

D. $\frac{125}{64}$

$x^3 = \frac{5 \cdot 5 \cdot 5}{8 \cdot 8 \cdot 8}$

32) What is the median of these numbers? 2, 27, 28, 19, 67, 44, 35

A. 19

B. 28

C. 44

D. 35

$2, 19, 27, (28), 35, 44, 67$

33) Right triangle ABC has two legs of lengths 6 cm (AB) and 8 cm (AC). What is the length of the third side (BC)?

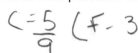

$10^2 = 100$

A. 4 cm

B. 6 cm

C. 8 cm

D. 10 cm

34) What is the equivalent temperature of 104°F in Celsius?

$C = \frac{5}{9}(F - 32)$

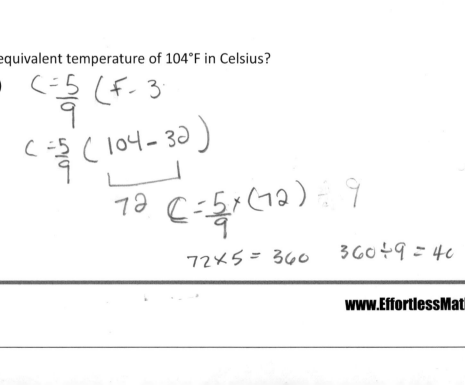

A. 32

B. 40

C. 48

D. 52

$C = \frac{5}{9}(F - 32)$

$C = \frac{5}{9}(104 - 32)$

$72 \quad C = \frac{5}{9} \times (72) \div 9$

$72 \times 5 = 360 \qquad 360 \div 9 = 40$

$*$ $=$ Out of $\rightarrow$ $\div$

35) If 40% of a number is 4, what is the number?

   A. 4

$\dfrac{.4x}{.4} = \dfrac{4}{.4}$

$\begin{array}{r} 200 \\ .4\, \overline{\smash{\big)}\ 80.0} \end{array}$

   B. 8

   C. 10

$x = 10$

80

   D. 12

36) The circle graph below shows all Mr. Green's expenses for last month. If he spent $660 on his car, how much did he spend for his rent?

   A. $700 $22? = 27 \cdot 660$

   B. $740 $\dfrac{22?}{22} = \dfrac{17820}{22}$

   C. $780

   D. $810 $? = 810$

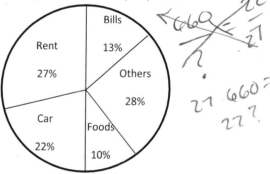

Mr. Green's monthly expenses

Bills 13%
Rent 27%
Others 28%
Car 22%
Foods 10%

$27 \cdot 660 = 22?$

37) Jason is 9 miles ahead of Joe running at 5.5 miles per hour and Joe is running at the speed of 7 miles per hour. How long does it take Joe to catch Jason?

   A. 3 hours $\dfrac{7 - 5.5 = 1.5\,mil}{9}$

   B. 4 hours

   C. 6 hours

   D. 8 hours

38) 55 students took an exam and 11 of them failed. What percent of the students passed the exam?

$\dfrac{part}{whole} = \dfrac{44}{55} = \dfrac{4}{5} = .8 \Leftarrow 80$

A. 20%

B. 40%

C. 60%

D. 80%

39) A bank is offering 3.5% simple interest on a savings account. If you deposit $12,000, how much interest will you earn in two years?

$A = 12,000\,(1+.035)^2$

A. $420

12,851.7

B. $840

$12000 \cdot .035 \cdot 2 \quad \$840$

C. $4200

interest = p·r·t

D. $8400

40) Simplify $6x^2y^3(2x^2y)^3 =$

A. $12x^4y^6$

B. $12x^8y^6$

$y^x \cdot y^z = y^{x+z}$

C. $48x^4y^6$

D. $48x^8y^6$

$(y^x)^z = y^{zx}$

IF YOU FINISH BEFORE TIME IS CALLED, YOU MAY CHECK YOUR WORK ON THIS SECTION ONLY. DO NOT TURN TO OTHER SECTION IN THE TEST.

STOP

TASC Mathematics
Practice Test 2

Section 2

(No Calculator)

12 questions

Total time for this section: 55 Minutes

You may NOT use a calculator on this Section.

41) $[-3 \times (-14) - 48] - (-14) + [3 \times 8] \div 2 = ?$

42) A tree 32 feet tall casts a shadow 12 feet long. Jack is 6 feet tall. How long is Jack's shadow?

43) What is the product of all possible values of x added to 30 in the following equation?

$$|2x - 6| = 12$$

44) What is the slope of a line that is perpendicular to the line $3x + y = 6$?

45) What is the value of the expression $3(x - 2y) + (2 - x)^2$ when $x = 5$ and $y = -3$?

46) What is the value of x in the following equation? $-60 = 115 - x$

47) The area of a rectangular yard is 90 square meters. What is its width if its length is 15 meters?

48) If $4x - 1 = 9$, what is the value of $2x + 10$?

49) The average weight of 18 girls in a class is 60 kg and the average weight of 32 boys in the same class is 62 kg. What is the average weight of all the 50 students in that class?

50) The width of a box is one third of its length. The height of the box is one third of its width. If the length of the box is 27 cm, what is the volume of the box?

51) In a classroom of 60 students, 42 are female. What percentage of the class is male?

52) Two third of 18 is equal to $\frac{2}{5}$ of what number?

TASC Mathematics Practice Tests Answers and Explanations

✳Now, it's time to review your results to see where you went wrong and what areas you need to improve!

TASC Mathematics Practice Tests Answer Key														
TASC Practice Test 1								**TASC Practice Test 2**						
Section 1				Section 2		Section 1						Section 2		
1	C	16	B	31	D	41	**25.5**	1	C	16	B	31	C	41	**20**
2	A	17	C	32	B	42	**18**	2	A	17	B	32	B	42	**2.25**
3	C	18	C	33	C	43	**130**	3	C	18	D	33	D	43	**3**
4	C	19	C	34	C	44	**140**	4	D	19	C	34	B	44	**1/3**
5	C	20	C	35	C	45	**2**	5	D	20	B	35	C	45	**42**
6	C	21	D	36	B	46	**90**	6	C	21	A	36	D	46	**175**
7	D	22	C	37	C	47	**2**	7	A	22	A	37	C	47	**6**
8	A	23	B	38	B	48	**10**	8	C	23	B	38	D	48	**15**
9	A	24	B	39	D	49	**33**	9	A	24	D	39	B	49	**61.28**
10	C	25	D	40	A	50	**0.04**	10	A	25	B	40	D	50	**729**
11	D	26	C			51	**16**	11	A	26	C			51	**30**
12	B	27	B			52	**24**	12	D	27	A			52	**30**
13	D	28	C					13	C	28	D				
14	D	29	B					14	B	29	D				
15	C	30	B					15	D	30	C				

TASC Mathematics Practice Test 1

Answers and Explanations

Section 1

1) **Choice C is correct**

Let x be the number. Write the equation and solve for x.

$(24 - x) \div x = 3$

Multiply both sides by x.

$(24 - x) = 3x$, then add x both sides. $24 = 4x$, now divide both sides by 4.

$x = 6$

2) **Choice A is correct**

The sum of supplement angles is 180. Let x be that angle. Therefore,

$x + 9x = 180$

$10x = 180$, divide both sides by 10: $x = 18$

3) **Choice C is correct**

The average speed of john is: $150 \div 6 = 25 \ km$

The average speed of Alice is: $180 \div 4 = 45 \ km$

Write the ratio and simplify.

$25 : 45 \Rightarrow 5 : 9$

4) **Choice C is correct**

$\$9 \times 10 = \$90$,   Petrol use: $10 \times 2 = 20$ liters

Petrol cost: $20 \times \$1 = \$20$

Money earned: $\$90 - \$20 = \$70$

5) Choice C is correct

$$\text{average} = \frac{\text{sum of terms}}{\text{number of terms}} = \frac{17 + 13 + 7 + 21 + 22}{5} = \frac{80}{5} = 16$$

6) Choice C is correct

Let x be the original price.

If the price of the sofa is decreased by 15% to \$476, then: 85% of $x = 476 \Rightarrow 0.85x = 476 \Rightarrow x = 476 \div 0.85 = 560$

7) Choice D is correct

Use Pythagorean Theorem: $a^2 + b^2 = c^2$

$9^2 + 12^2 = c^2 \Rightarrow 81 + 144 = c^2 \Rightarrow 225 = c^2 \Rightarrow c = 15$

8) Choice A is correct

The percent of girls playing tennis is: $40\% \times 25\% = 0.40 \times 0.25 = 0.10 = 10\%$

9) Choice A is correct

Area of the circle is less than $16\,\pi$. Use the formula of areas of circles.

$$Area = \pi r^2 \Rightarrow 64\,\pi > \pi r^2 \Rightarrow 64 > r^2 \Rightarrow r < 8$$

Radius of the circle is less than 8. Let's put 8 for the radius. Now, use the circumference formula: $Circumference = 2\pi r = 2\pi\,(8) = 16\,\pi$

Since the radius of the circle is less than 8. Then, the circumference of the circle must be less than $16\,\pi$. Only choice A is less than $16\,\pi$.

10) Choice C is correct

$\begin{cases} x + 4y = 10 \\ 5x + 10y = 20 \end{cases} \rightarrow$ Multiply the top equation by -5 then,

$\begin{cases} -5x - 20y = -50 \\ 5x + 10y = 20 \end{cases} \rightarrow$ Add two equations

$-10y = -30 \rightarrow y = 3$, plug in the value of y into the first equation

$$x + 4y = 10 \rightarrow x + 4(3) = 10 \rightarrow x + 12 = 10$$

Subtract 12 from both sides of the equation. Then: $x + 12 = 10 \rightarrow x = -2$

11) Choice D is correct

Write the equation and solve for B:

$0.60\ A = 0.20\ B$, divide both sides by 0.20, then:

$0.60/0.20\ A = B$, therefore:

$B = 3A$, and B is 3 times of A or it's 300% of A.

12) Choice B is correct

Use this formula: Percent of Change

$$\frac{New\ Value - Old\ Value}{Old\ Value} \times 100\%$$

$\frac{16000 - 20000}{20000} \times 100\% = 20\%$ and $\frac{12800 - 16000}{16000} \times 100\% = 20\%$

13) Choice D is correct

If the length of the box is 27, then the width of the box is one third of it, 9, and the height of the box is 3 (one third of the width). The volume of the box is:

$V = lwh = (27)\ (9)\ (3) = 729$

14) Choice D is correct

To find the number of possible outfit combinations, multiply number of options for each factor: $6 \times 3 \times 5 = 90$

15) Choice C is correct

Use simple interest formula: $I = prt$

$(I = interest, \quad p = principal, \quad r = rate, \quad t = time)$

$$I = (8,000)(0.045)(5) = 1,800$$

16) Choice B is correct

$6^4 = 6 \times 6 \times 6 \times 6 = 1,296$

17) Choice C is correct

Use percent formula:

$$part = \frac{percent}{100} \times whole$$

$25 = \frac{percent}{100} \times 20 \Rightarrow 25 = \frac{percent \times 20}{100} \Rightarrow 25 = \frac{percent \times 2}{10}$, multiply both sides by 10.

$250 = percent \times 2$, divide both sides by 2.

$125 = percent$

18) Choice C is correct

The area of the trapezoid is:

$$Area = \frac{1}{2}h(b_1 + b_2) = \frac{1}{2}(x)(13 + 8) = 126$$

$$\rightarrow 10.5x = 126 \rightarrow x = 12$$

$$y = \sqrt{5^2 + 12^2} = \sqrt{25 + 144} = \sqrt{169} = 13$$

The perimeter of the trapezoid is: $12 + 13 + 8 + 13 = 46$

19) Choice C is correct

Add the first 5 numbers. 40 + 45 + 50 + 35 + 55 = 225

To find the distance traveled in the next 5 hours, multiply the average by number of hours.

Distance = Average × Rate = 50 × 5 = 250

Add both numbers.

250 + 225 = 475

20) Choice C is correct

Use distance formula:

Distance = Rate × time $\Rightarrow$ 420 = 50 × T, divide both sides by 50. 420 / 50 = T $\Rightarrow$ T = 8.4 hours.

Change hours to minutes for the decimal part. 0.4 hours = 0.4 × 60 = 24 minutes.

21) Choice D is correct

The equation of a line is in the form of $y = mx + b$, where m is the slope of the line and b is the $y - intercept$ of the line.

Two points (4,3) and (3,2) are on line A. Therefore, the slope of the line A is:

$$slope\ of\ line\ A = \frac{y_2 - y_1}{x_2 - x_1} = \frac{2-3}{3-4} = \frac{-1}{-1} = 1$$

The slope of line A is 1. Thus, the formula of the line A is:

$y = mx + b = x + b$, choose a point and plug in the values of x and y in the equation to solve for b. Let's choose point (4, 3). Then:

$$y = x + b \to 3 = 4 + b \to b = 3 - 4 = -1$$

The equation of line A is: $y = x - 1$

Now, let's review the choices provided:

A. $(-1, 2)$ $y = x - 1 \to 2 = -1 - 1 = -2$ This is not true.

B. $(5, 7)$ $y = x - 1 \to 7 = 5 - 1 = 4$ This is not true.

C. $(3, 4)$ $y = x - 1 \to 4 = 3 - 1 = 2$ This is not true.

D. $(-1, -2)$ $y = x - 1 \to -2 = -1 - 1 = -2$ This is true!

22) Choice C is correct

Let x be the number. Write the equation and solve for x.

$\frac{2}{3} \times 18 = \frac{2}{5} \cdot x \Rightarrow \frac{2 \times 18}{3} = \frac{2x}{5}$, use cross multiplication to solve for x.

$$5 \times 36 = 2x \times 3 \Rightarrow 180 = 6x \Rightarrow x = 30$$

23) Choice B is correct

To find the discount, multiply the number by (100% − rate of discount).

Therefore, for the first discount we get: (D) (100% − 20%) = (D) (0.80) = 0.80 D

For increase of 10 %: (0.85 D) (100% + 10%) = (0.85 D) (1.10) = 0.88 D = 88% of D

24) Choice B is correct

Use the formula for Percent of Change

$$\frac{New\ Value - Old\ Value}{Old\ Value} \times 100\%$$

$\frac{28-40}{40} \times 100\% = -30\%$ (Negative sign here means that the new price is less than old price).

25) Choices D is correct

Some of prime numbers are: 2, 3, 5, 7, 11, 13

Find the product of two consecutive prime numbers:

$2 \times 3 = 6$ (not in the options)

$3 \times 5 = 15$ (bingo!)

$5 \times 7 = 35$ (not in the options)

$7 \times 11 = 77$ (not in the options)

26) Choice C is correct

Let's compare each fraction:

$$\frac{2}{7} < \frac{3}{8} < \frac{5}{11} < \frac{3}{4}$$

Only choice C provides the right order.

27) Choice B is correct

Use the information provided in the question to draw the shape.

Use Pythagorean Theorem: $a^2 + b^2 = c^2$

$40^2 + 30^2 = c^2 \Rightarrow 1600 + 900 = c^2 \Rightarrow 2500 = c^2 \Rightarrow c = 50$

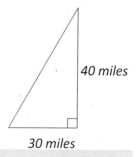

40 miles

30 miles

28) Choice C is correct

The ratio of boy to girls is 4:7. Therefore, there are 4 boys out of 11 students. To find the answer, first divide the total number of students by 11, then multiply the result by 4.

$44 \div 11 = 4 \Rightarrow 4 \times 4 = 16$

There are 16 boys and 28 ($44 - 16$) girls. So, 12 more boys should be enrolled to make the ratio 1:1

29) Choice B is correct

The question is this: 530.40 is what percent of 624?

Use percent formula:

$$part = \frac{percent}{100} \times whole$$

$$530.40 = \frac{percent}{100} \times 624 \Rightarrow 530.40 = \frac{percent \times 624}{100} \Rightarrow 53040 = percent \times 624 \Rightarrow$$

$$percent = \frac{53040}{624} = 85$$

530.40 is 85 % of 624. Therefore, the discount is: $100\% - 85\% = 15\%$

30) Choice B is correct

If the score of Mia was 60, therefore the score of Ava is 30. Since, the score of Emma was half as that of Ava, therefore, the score of Emma is 15.

31) Choice D is correct

If 17 balls are removed from the bag at random, there will be one ball in the bag.

The probability of choosing a brown ball is 1 out of 18. Therefore, the probability of not choosing a brown ball is 17 out of 18 and the probability of having not a brown ball after removing 17 balls is the same.

32) Choice B is correct

Let x be the smallest number. Then, these are the numbers:

$$x, x + 1, x + 2, x + 3, x + 4$$

$$\text{average} = \frac{\text{sum of terms}}{\text{number of terms}} \Rightarrow 38 = \frac{x+(x+1)+(x+2)+(x+3)+(x+4)}{5} \Rightarrow 38 = \frac{5x+10}{5} \Rightarrow 190 = 5x + 10$$
$$\Rightarrow$$

$$180 = 5x \Rightarrow x = 36$$

33) Choice C is correct

The area of the floor is: 6 cm × 24 cm = 144 cm^2

The number of tiles needed = 144 ÷ 8 = 18

34) Choice C is correct

The weight of 12.2 meters of this rope is: $12.2 \times 600 \, g = 7,320 \, g$

1 kg = 1,000 g, therefore, $7,320 \, g \div 1000 = 7.32 \, kg$

35) Choice C is correct

4% of the volume of the solution is alcohol. Let x be the volume of the solution.

Then: $4\% \ of \ x = 24 \ ml \Rightarrow 0.04 \ x = 24 \Rightarrow x = 24 \div 0.04 = 600$

36) Choice B is correct

$$\text{average} = \frac{\text{sum of terms}}{\text{number of terms}}$$

The sum of the weight of all girls is: $18 \times 60 = 1080 \ kg$

The sum of the weight of all boys is: $32 \times 62 = 1984 \ kg$

The sum of the weight of all students is: $1080 + 1984 = 3064 \ kg$

$$\text{average} = \frac{3064}{50} = 61.28$$

37) Choice C is correct

Let x be the original price.

If the price of a laptop is decreased by 10% to \$360, then:

$90 \ \% \ of \ x = 360 \Rightarrow 0.90x = 360 \Rightarrow x = 360 \div 0.90 = 400$

38) Choice B is correct

Write the numbers in order:

4, 5, 8, 9, 13, 15, 18

Since we have 7 numbers (7 is odd), then the median is the number in the middle, which is 9.

39) Choice D is correct

Formula for the Surface area of a cylinder is:

$$SA = 2\pi r^2 + 2\pi rh \rightarrow 150\pi = 2\pi r^2 + 2\pi r(10) \rightarrow r^2 + 10r - 75 = 0$$

$$(r + 15)(r - 5) = 0 \rightarrow r = 5 \quad or \quad r = -15 \ (unacceptable)$$

40) Choice A is correct

Let x be the number of years. Therefore, \$2,000 per year equals $2000x$.

starting from $24,000 annual salary means you should add that amount to $2000x$.

Income more than that is:

$I > 2000x + 24000$

TASC Mathematics Practice Test 1

Section 2

41) The answer is 25.5

$3x - 5 = 8.5 \rightarrow 3x = 8.5 + 5 = 13.5 \rightarrow x = \frac{13.5}{3} = 4.5$

Then; $5x + 3 = 5 (4.5) + 3 = 22.5 + 3 = 25.5$

42) The answer is 18

First draw an isosceles triangle. Remember that two sides of the triangle are equal.

Isosceles right triangle

Let put a for the legs. Then:

$a = 6 \Rightarrow$ area of the triangle is $= \frac{1}{2}(6 \times 6) = \frac{36}{2} = 18$

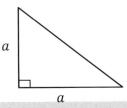

43) The answer is 130

The perimeter of the trapezoid is 54.

Therefore, the missing side (height) is $= 54 - 18 - 12 - 14 = 10$

Area of a trapezoid: $A = \frac{1}{2} h (b_1 + b_2) = \frac{1}{2} (10) (12 + 14) = 130$

44) The answer is 140

The question is this: 1.75 is what percent of 1.25?

Use percent formula:

$$\text{part} = \frac{\text{percent}}{100} \times \text{whole}$$

$$1.75 = \frac{\text{percent}}{100} \times 1.25 \Rightarrow 1.75 = \frac{\text{percent} \times 1.25}{100} \Rightarrow 175 = \text{percent} \times 1.25 \Rightarrow \text{percent} = \frac{175}{1.25} = 140$$

45) The answer is 2

Use PEMDAS (order of operation):

$$-18 + 6 \times (-5) - [4 + 22 \times (-4)] \div 2 + 8 = -18 - 30 - [4 - 88] \div 2 + 8$$
$$= -48 - [-84] \div 2 + 8 = -48 + 84 \div 2 + 8 = -48 + 42 + 8 = 2$$

46) The answer is 90

The relationship among all sides of special right triangle

$30° - 60° - 90°$ is provided in this triangle:

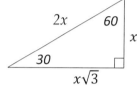

In this triangle, the opposite side of 30° angle is half of the hypotenuse.

Draw the shape of this question.

The latter is the hypotenuse. Therefore, the latter is 90 feet.

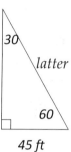

47) The answer is 2

Let x be the length of an edge of cube, then the volume of a cube is: $V = x^3$

The surface area of cube is: $SA = 6x^2$

The volume of cube A is $\frac{1}{3}$ of its surface area. Then:

$x^3 = \frac{6x^2}{3} \to x^3 = 2x^2$, divide both side of the equation by x^2. Then:

$$\frac{x^3}{x^2} = \frac{3x^2}{x^2} \to x = 2$$

48) The answer is 10

The input value is 5. Then: $x = 5$

$$f(x) = x^2 - 3x \to f(5) = 5^2 - 3(5) = 25 - 15 = 10$$

49) The answer is 33

Since $N = 6$, substitute 6 for N in the equation $\frac{x-3}{5} = N$, which gives $\frac{x-3}{5} = 6$.

Multiplying both sides of $\frac{x-3}{5} = 6$ by 5 gives $x - 3 = 30$ and then adding 3 to both sides of

$x - 3 = 30$ then, $x = 33$.

50) The answer is $\frac{1}{25}$ or 0.04

Write the ratio of $5a$ to $2b$.

$$\frac{5a}{2b} = \frac{1}{10}$$

Use cross multiplication and then simplify.

$$5a \times 10 = 2b \times 1 \rightarrow 50a = 2b \rightarrow a = \frac{2b}{50} = \frac{b}{25}$$

Now, find the ratio of a to b.

$$\frac{a}{b} = \frac{\frac{b}{25}}{b} \rightarrow \frac{b}{25} \div b = \frac{b}{25} \times \frac{1}{b} = \frac{b}{25b} = \frac{1}{25} = 0.04$$

51) The answer is 16

The rate of construction company$= \frac{30 \text{ cm}}{1 \text{ min}} = 30$ cm/min

Height of the wall after 40 minutes $= \frac{30 \text{ cm}}{1 \text{ min}} \times 40 \text{ min} = 1200$ cm

Let x be the height of wall, then $\frac{3}{4}x = 1200$ cm$\rightarrow x = \frac{4 \times 1200}{3} \rightarrow x = 1600$ cm $= 16 \ m$

52) The answer is 24

$$\text{average} = \frac{\text{sum of terms}}{\text{number of terms}} \Rightarrow 18 = \frac{13+15+20+x}{4} \Rightarrow 72 = 48 + x \Rightarrow x = 24$$

TASC Mathematics Practice Test 2

Answers and Explanations

Section 1

1) Choice C is correct

$3^6 = 3 \times 3 \times 3 \times 3 \times 3 \times 3 = 729$

2) Choice A is correct

Simplify and combine like terms.

$(6x^3 - 8x^2 + 2x^4) - (4x^2 - 2x^4 + 2x^3) \Rightarrow (6x^3 - 8x^2 + 2x^4) - 4x^2 + 2x^4 - 2x^3 \Rightarrow$

$$4x^4 + 4x^3 - 12x^2$$

3) Choice C is correct

The population is increased by 15% and 20%. 15% increase changes the population to 115% of original population.

For the second increase, multiply the result by 120%.

$(1.15) \times (1.20) = 1.38 = 138\%$

38 percent of the population is increased after two years.

4) Choice D is correct

Solve for x.

$-2 \le 2x - 4 < 8 \Rightarrow$ (add 4 all sides) $-2 + 4 \le 2x - 4 + 4 < 8 + 4 \Rightarrow$

$2 \le 2x < 12 \Rightarrow$ (divide all sides by 2) $1 \le x < 6$

x is between 1 and 6. Choice D represent this inequality.

5) Choice D is correct

$Volume\ of\ a\ box = length \times width \times height = 4 \times 5 \times 6 = 120$

6) Choice C is correct

To find the number of possible outfit combinations, multiply number of options for each factor:

$3 \times 5 \times 4 = 60$

7) Choice A is correct

In the stadium the ratio of home fans to visiting fans in a crowd is 5:7. Therefore, total number of fans must be divisible by 12: 5 + 7 = 12.
Let's review the choices:
A. 12,324: $12,324 \div 12 = 1,027$

B. 42,326 $42,326 \div 12 = 3,527.166$

C. 44,566 $44,566 \div 12 = 3,713.833$

D. 66,812 $66,812 \div 12 = 5,567.666$

Only choice A when divided by 12 results a whole number.

8) Choice C is correct

Three times of 24,000 is 72,000. One sixth of them cancelled their tickets.

One sixth of 72,000 equals 12,000 ($\frac{1}{6} \times 72000 = 12000$).

60,000(72,000 – 12,000 = 60,000) fans are attending this week

9) Choice A is correct

The area of the square is 595.36. Therefore, the side of the square is square root of the area.

$\sqrt{595.36} = 24.4$

Four times the side of the square is the perimeter:

$4 \times 24.4 = 97.6$

10) Choice A is correct

$x + 2y = 4$. Plug in the values of x and y from choices provided. Then:

A. $(-2, 3)$ $x + 2y = 4 \rightarrow -2 + 2(3) = 4 \rightarrow -2 + 6 = 4$ This is true!

B. $(1, 2)$ $x + 2y = 4 \rightarrow 1 + 2(2) = 4 \rightarrow 1 + 4 = 4$ This is NOT true!

C. $(-1, 3)$ $x + 2y = 4 \rightarrow -1 + 2(3) = 4 \rightarrow -1 + 6 = 4$ This is NOT true!

D. $(-3, 4)$ $x + 2y = 4 \rightarrow -3 + 2(4) = 4 \rightarrow -3 + 8 = 4$ This is NOT true!

11) Choice A is correct

The width of the rectangle is twice its length. Let x be the length. Then, $width = 2x$

Perimeter of the rectangle is 2 (width + length) = $2(2x + x) = 60 \Rightarrow 6x = 60 \Rightarrow x = 10$

Length of the rectangle is 10 meters.

12) Choice D is correct

Change the numbers to decimal and then compare.

$\frac{2}{3} = 0.666 \ldots$

0.68

$67\% = 0.67$

$\frac{4}{5} = 0.80$

Then:

$$\frac{2}{3} < 67\% < 0.68 < \frac{4}{5}$$

13) Choice C is correct

average (mean) $= \frac{\text{sum of terms}}{\text{number of terms}} \Rightarrow 88 = \frac{\text{sum of terms}}{50} \Rightarrow sum = 88 \times 50 = 4400$

The difference of 94 and 69 is 25. Therefore, 25 should be subtracted from the sum.

$4400 - 25 = 4375$

mean $= \frac{\text{sum of terms}}{\text{number of terms}} \Rightarrow$ mean $= \frac{4375}{50} = 87.5$

14) Choice B is correct

To get a sum of 6 for two dice, we can get 5 different options:

(5, 1), (4, 2), (3, 3), (2, 4), (1, 5)

To get a sum of 9 for two dice, we can get 4 different options:

(6, 3), (5, 4), (4, 5), (3, 6)

Therefore, there are 9 options to get the sum of 6 or 9.

Since, we have 6 × 6 = 36 total options, the probability of getting a sum of 6 and 9 is 9 out of 36 or $\frac{1}{4}$.

15) Choice D is correct

Use formula of rectangle prism volume.

$V = (length)(width)(height) \Rightarrow 2000 = (25)(10)(height) \Rightarrow$

$height = 2000 \div 250 = 8$

16) Choice B is correct

The diagonal of the square is 8. Let x be the side.

Use Pythagorean Theorem: $a^2 + b^2 = c^2$

$x^2 + x^2 = 8^2 \Rightarrow 2x^2 = 8^2 \Rightarrow 2x^2 = 64 \Rightarrow x^2 = 32 \Rightarrow x = \sqrt{32}$

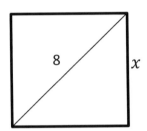

The area of the square is:

$\sqrt{32} \times \sqrt{32} = 32$

17) Choice B is correct

$$\text{Probability} = \frac{number\ of\ desired\ outcomes}{number\ of\ total\ outcomes} = \frac{18}{12+18+18+24} = \frac{18}{72} = \frac{1}{4}$$

18) Choice D is correct

$$\text{average} = \frac{\text{sum of terms}}{\text{number of terms}} \Rightarrow (\text{average of 6 numbers}) \ 12 = \frac{\text{sum of numbers}}{6} \Rightarrow \text{sum of 6 numbers is}$$

12 × 6 = 72

(average of 4 numbers) $10 = \frac{\text{sum of numbers}}{4} \Rightarrow$ sum of 4 numbers is 10 × 4 = 40

sum of 6 numbers − sum of 4 numbers = sum of 2 numbers

72 − 40 = 32

average of 2 numbers $= \frac{32}{2} = 16$

19) Choice C is correct

Solving Systems of Equations by Elimination

Multiply the first equation by (−2), then add it to the second equation.

$$\begin{array}{l} -2(2x + 5y = 11) \\ \underline{4x - 2y = -14} \end{array} \Rightarrow \begin{array}{l} -4x - 10y = -22 \\ \underline{4x - 2y = -14} \end{array} \Rightarrow -12y = -36 \Rightarrow y = 3$$

Plug in the value of y into one of the equations and solve for x.

$$2x + 5(3) = 11 \Rightarrow 2x + 15 = 11 \Rightarrow 2x = -4 \Rightarrow x = -2$$

20) Choice B is correct

The perimeter of the trapezoid is 36 cm.

Therefore, the missing side (height) is $= 36 - 8 - 12 - 6 = 10$

Area of a trapezoid: $A = \frac{1}{2}h(b_1 + b_2) = \frac{1}{2}(10)(6 + 8) = 70$

21) Choice A is correct

First, find the number.

Let x be the number. Write the equation and solve for x.

150 % of a number is 75, then:

$$1.5 \times x = 75 \Rightarrow x = 75 \div 1.5 = 50$$

90 % of 50 is: $\qquad 0.9 \times 50 = 45$

22) Choice A is correct

Let x be the number of new shoes the team can purchase. Therefore, the team can purchase $120\,x$.

The team had $20,000 and spent $14,000. Now the team can spend on new shoes $6,000 at most.

Now, write the inequality:

$$120x + 14,000 \leq 20,000$$

23) Choice B is correct

The probability of choosing a Hearts is $\frac{13}{52} = \frac{1}{4}$

24) Choice D is correct

First, find the sum of five numbers.

$$\text{average} = \frac{\text{sum of terms}}{\text{number of terms}} \Rightarrow 24 = \frac{\text{sum of 5 numbers}}{5} \Rightarrow \text{sum of 5 numbers} = 24 \times 5 = 120$$

The sum of 5 numbers is 120. If a sixth number that is greater than 42 is added to these numbers, then the sum of 6 numbers must be greater than 162.

$$120 + 42 = 162$$

If the number was 42, then the average of the numbers is:

$$\text{average} = \frac{\text{sum of terms}}{\text{number of terms}} = \frac{162}{6} = 27$$

Since the number is bigger than 42. Then, the average of six numbers must be greater than 27. Choice D is greater than 27.

25) Choice B is correct

Let L be the length of the rectangular and W be the with of the rectangular. Then,

$$L = 4W + 3$$

The perimeter of the rectangle is 36 meters. Therefore: $2L + 2W = 36$

$$L + W = 18$$

Replace the value of L from the first equation into the second equation and solve for W:

$$(4W + 3) + W = 18 \rightarrow 5W + 3 = 18 \rightarrow 5W = 15 \rightarrow W = 3$$

The width of the rectangle is 3 meters and its length is:

$$L = 4W + 3 = 4(3) + 3 = 15$$

The area of the rectangle is: length × width = 3 × 15 = 45

26) Choice C is correct

Th ratio of boy to girls is 4:7. Therefore, there are 4 boys out of 11 students. To find the answer, first divide the total number of students by 11, then multiply the result by 4.

$$44 \div 11 = 4 \Rightarrow 4 \times 4 = 16$$

There are 16 boys and 28 (44 − 16) girls. So, 12 more boys should be enrolled to make the ratio 1:1

27) Choice A is correct

2,500 out of 55,000 equals to $\dfrac{2500}{55000} = \dfrac{25}{550} = \dfrac{1}{22}$

28) Choice D is correct

Jason needs an 75% average to pass for five exams. Therefore, the sum of 5 exams must be at lease 5 × 75 = 375

The sum of 4 exams is: $68 + 72 + 85 + 90 = 315$

The minimum score Jason can earn on his fifth and final test to pass is: $375 - 315 = 60$

29) Choice D is correct

Isolate and solve for x.

$$\frac{2}{3}x + \frac{1}{6} = \frac{1}{3} \Rightarrow \frac{2}{3}x = \frac{1}{3} - \frac{1}{6} = \frac{1}{6} \Rightarrow \frac{2}{3}x = \frac{1}{6}$$

Multiply both sides by the reciprocal of the coefficient of x.

$$\left(\frac{3}{2}\right)\frac{2}{3}x = \frac{1}{6}\left(\frac{3}{2}\right) \Rightarrow x = \frac{3}{12} = \frac{1}{4}$$

30) Choice C is correct

Surface Area of a cylinder = 2πr (r + h),

The radius of the cylinder is 3 (6 ÷ 2) inches and its height is 8 inches. Therefore,

Surface Area of a cylinder = 2π (3) (3 + 8) = 66 π

31) Choice C is correct

The square of a number is $\frac{25}{64}$, then the number is the square root of $\frac{25}{64}$

$$\sqrt{\frac{25}{64}} = \frac{5}{8}$$

The cube of the number is:

$$\left(\frac{5}{8}\right)^3 = \frac{125}{512}$$

32) Choice B is correct

Write the numbers in order: 2, 19, 27, 28, 35, 44, 67

Median is the number in the middle. So, the median is 28.

33) Choice D is correct

Use Pythagorean Theorem: $a^2 + b^2 = c^2$

$6^2 + 8^2 = c^2 \Rightarrow 100 = c^2 \Rightarrow c = 10$

34) Choice B is correct

Plug in 104 for F and then solve for C.

$$C = \frac{5}{9}(F - 32) \Rightarrow C = \frac{5}{9}(104 - 32) \Rightarrow C = \frac{5}{9}(72) = 40$$

35) Choice C is correct

Let x be the number. Write the equation and solve for x.

$$40\% \ of \ x = 4 \Rightarrow 0.40 \ x = 4 \Rightarrow x = 4 \div 0.40 = 10$$

36) Choice D is correct

Let x be all expenses, then $\frac{22}{100} x = \$660 \rightarrow x = \frac{100 \times \$660}{22} = \$3,000$

He spent for his rent: $\frac{27}{100} \times \$3,000 = \$810$

37) Choice C is correct

The distance between Jason and Joe is 9 miles. Jason running at 5.5 miles per hour and Joe is running at the speed of 7 miles per hour. Therefore, every hour the distance is 1.5 miles less. $9 \div 1.5 = 6$

38) Choice D is correct

The failing rate is 11 out of $55 = \frac{11}{55}$

Change the fraction to percent:

$$\frac{11}{55} \times 100\% = 20\%$$

20 percent of students failed. Therefore, 80 percent of students passed the exam.

39) Choice B is correct

Use simple interest formula:

$$I = prt$$

(I = interest, p = principal, r = rate, t = time)

$$I = (12000)(0.035)(2) = 840$$

40) Choice D is correct

Simplify.

$$6x^2y^3(2x^2y)^3 = 6x^2y^3(8x^6y^3) = 48x^8y^6$$

TASC Mathematics Practice Test 1 2

Section 2

41) The answer is 20

Use PEMDAS (order of operation):

$$[-3 \times (-14) - 48] - (-14) + [3 \times 8] \div 2 = [42 - 48] + 14 + 24 \div 2 = -6 + 14 + 12$$
$$= 20$$

42) The answer is 2.25

Write a proportion and solve for the missing number.

$\frac{32}{12} = \frac{6}{x} \rightarrow 32x = 6 \times 12 = 72$

$$32x = 72 \rightarrow x = \frac{72}{32} = 2.25$$

43) The answer is 3

To solve absolute values equations, write two equations.

$2x - 6$ can equal positive 12, or negative 12. Therefore,

$$2x - 6 = 12 \Rightarrow 2x = 18 \Rightarrow x = 9$$

$$2x - 6 = -12 \Rightarrow 2x = -12 + 6 = -6 \Rightarrow x = -3$$

Find the product of solutions: $-3 \times 12 = -27$

$-27 + 30 = 3$

44) The answer is $\frac{1}{3}$

The equation of a line in slope intercept form is: $y = \text{m}x + b$

Solve for y.

$$3x + y = 6 \rightarrow y = -3x + 6$$

The slope of this line is -3.

The product of the slopes of two perpendicular lines is -1. Therefore, the slope of a line that is perpendicular to this line is:

$$m_1 \times m_2 = -1 \Rightarrow -3 \times m_2 = -1 \Rightarrow m_2 = \frac{-1}{-3} = \frac{1}{3}$$

45) The answer is 42

Plug in the value of x and y. $3(x - 2y) + (2 - x)^2$ when $x = 5$ and $y = -3$

$x = 5$ and $y = -3$

$3(x - 2y) + (2 - x)^2 = 3(5 - 2(-3)) + (2 - 5)^2 = 3(5 + 6) + (-3)^2 = 33 + 9 = 42$

46) The answer is 175

$-60 = 115 - x$

First, subtract 115 from both sides of the equation. Then:
$-60 - 115 = 115 - 115 - x \rightarrow -175 = -x$

Multiply both sides by (-1): $\rightarrow x = 175$

47) The answer is 6

Let y be the width of the rectangle. Then; $15 \times y = 90 \rightarrow y = \frac{90}{15} = 6$

48) The answer is 15

$4x - 1 = 9 \rightarrow 4x = 9 + 1 = 10 \rightarrow x = \frac{10}{4} = 2.5$

Then, $2x + 10 = 2(2.5) + 10 = 5 + 10 = 15$

49) The answer is 61.28

Average $= \dfrac{\text{sum of terms}}{\text{number of terms}}$

The sum of the weight of all girls is: 18 × 60 = 1080 kg

The sum of the weight of all boys is: 32 × 62 = 1984 kg

The sum of the weight of all students is: 1080 + 1984 = 3064 kg

Average $= \dfrac{3064}{50} = 61.28$

50) The answer is 729

If the length of the box is 27, then the width of the box is one third of it, 9, and the height of the box is 3 (one third of the width). The volume of the box is:

$V = lwh = (27)(9)(3) = 729$

51) The answer is 30

Number of males in classroom is: $60 - 42 = 18$

Then, the percentage of males in the classroom is: $\frac{18}{60} \times 100 = 0.3 \times 100 = 30\%$

52) The answer is 30

Let x be the number. Write the equation and solve for x.

$\frac{2}{3} \times 18 = \frac{2}{5}x \to \frac{2 \times 18}{3} = \frac{2x}{5}$, use cross multiplication to solve for x.

$5 \times 36 = 2x \times 3 \Rightarrow 180 = 6x \Rightarrow x = 30$

"Effortless Math" Publications

Effortless Math authors' team strives to prepare and publish the best quality Mathematics learning resources to make learning Math easier for all. We hope that our publications help you or your student Math in an effective way.

We all in Effortless Math wish you good luck and successful studies!

Effortless Math Authors

www.EffortlessMath.com

... So Much More Online!

✓ FREE Math lessons

✓ More Math learning books!

✓ Mathematics Worksheets

✓ Online Math Tutors

Need a PDF version of this book?

Visit www.EffortlessMath.com